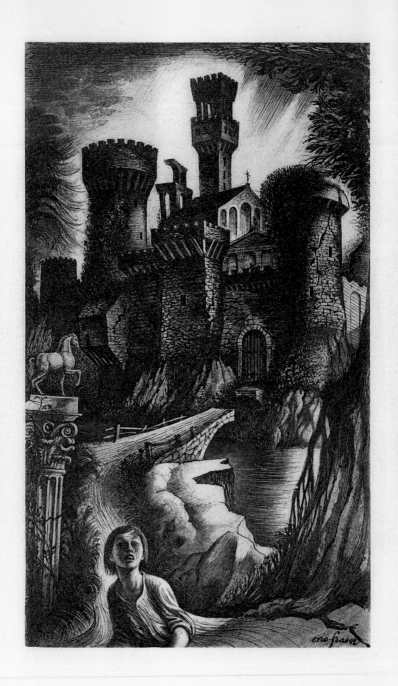

# THE
# CASTLE
# OF
# FRATTA

by Ippolito Nievo

In a Translation by
Lovett F. Edwards
Illustrations by
Eric Fraser

FOLIO SOCIETY

*First published* 1954
1954 *Copyright The Folio Society*

DISTRIBUTED IN THE UNITED STATES
BY PHILIP C. DUSCHNES, NEW YORK

*This book has been composed in 11 point Bodoni 1½ point leaded,
made and printed by William Clowes and Sons, Limited,
London and Beccles.*
*The illustrations have been printed by the Chiswick Press.*

# CONTENTS

iii

# V

# ILLUSTRATIONS

# INTRODUCTION

FROM the great terrace of the Castle of Montechiarugolo, one looked down over the stony bed of the Enza, a mere trickle in summer, a broad expanse of water when the snows melted in the Apennines. Below, was a sheer drop of some ninety feet. Behind, on the inner wall of the terrace, were fading coats of arms from some princely marriage scribbled over with the names of prisoners of many wars, ranging back for over a century. To these we added ours.

It was in this forbidding palace-prison that I first read the *Confessions*, that long epic of the loves of Carlo Altoviti and the Pisana of which *The Castle of Fratta* is the idyllic opening. At that time I knew nothing of the book nor of the author, but was at once struck by the sweep of the story and the lively vigour of the language, so different from the arid classicism of the older books and the banal puerilities of the later ones in the camp library.

I determined to find out if it had been translated and, if not, to translate it myself.

Nievo's style has the vigorous, and somewhat careless, sweep of a great writer who has something to say and very little time in which to say it. In that it reminds one of men so different in matter and yet so similar in manner as Dickens, Dostoyevsky or Dumas. The key to his racy and vivid style is to be found in an aside in the book itself: 'Our great authors,' he writes, 'I have guessed at rather than understood, loved rather than studied, and I must admit that the greater number of them have set my teeth on edge. I am aware that the fault must have been mine alone, but none the less I flatter myself that in the future he who writes will remember how he used to speak and that the aim of speaking is precisely to make one-self understood. Is it not far better to make oneself understood by the many than only by the few? In France they print, they sell and they read far more books than we do for no other reason than because of the universality of the language and the clarity of the discourse. With us, there are three or four vocabularies and the learned have the habit of employing the least used of them. As for logic, they use it as a springboard to make continuous leaps. . . . Those who are accustomed to ascend step by step remain a good half-mile behind and, having lost their guide from view, sit down contentedly to wait for another who perhaps may never come. .I speak ill of no one, but in writing think that many will have to read. In this way we shall see if our literature may perhaps afford an assistance greater than it has so far given to our national renaissance.'

Not only I myself, but many Italians who are critics of their literature, consider the *Confessions* as one of the finest novels in the Italian language, comparable only to Manzoni's *The Betrothed*. But Nievo has far more humour than Manzoni and also greatly exceeds him in the characterization of his leading women, the Pisana and Clara. It would be fair to say that the Pisana is the one really successful portrait of a woman in all Italian literature.

Nievo worked from life; and this live material is filled with humour about the customs, the society and the history of the times. 'The Castle of Fratta,' writes a leading critic, 'is the picture of an ancient and noble family of the past, anchored in times that have gone and defended from the outer world by a drawbridge that no longer serves any purpose. This little world has as its epicentre the kitchen, the great kitchen, immense and mysterious, of Fratta, dominated by the autocratic and formalist figure of the old Count, seated with his rusty sword and spurs, rigid in his great armchair. It has the charm of the most beautiful pages that can be found among the few great novels of Italian literature . . .'

*The Castle of Fratta* contains an exquisite account of the childish loves of Carlo and the Pisana, thrown into greater relief by the stormy secondary love affair of Clara and Lucilio. But the many subsidiary characters live in their own right and are described with a malicious humour that makes them live in the memory: the braggart Captain Sandracca, the otiose and

2

gourmand Monsignor Orlando, the primitive country doctor Sperandio and the arrogant feudal lord of Venchieredo.

Parallel with the love interest is the political interest, which is given in the first sentence of the book: 'I was born a Venetian on the 18th of September 1775, the Day of St. Luke the Evangelist, and I shall die, by the Grace of God, an Italian whenever the Providence that mysteriously controls our world shall so ordain.'

Born in Padua in 1831, Ippolito Nievo was one of those many-sided and colourful personalities so often considered typical of the Italian renaissance, but who were to spring up again in the stormy times of the risorgimento. Poet, philosopher, dreamer, conspirator and soldier, he crowded as much incident into the brief thirty years of his life as into the vast canvas of the *Confessions*.

His grandfather was the Venetian patrician, Carlo Marin, from whom he learnt while still a boy, during the long winter vigils at the ancestral castle of Colloredo in the Friuli, the events of the fall of Venice and the Napoleonic whirlwind that he was to evoke in the *Confessions*. It was near Portogruaro that he saw the ruins of that Castle of Fratta which he was to make live again in his masterpiece.

In 1847 Nievo was sent to the *liceo* of Mantua, where there was a considerable amount of clandestine student politics which, in those days, was equivalent to conspiracy. It seems that, while only seventeen, he joined the Mantuan Civil Guard. But Mantua did not attain even the ephemeral liberty of Venice or Milan, and the young poet, bitter and disillusioned, was sent by his father to Pisa on the pretext of learning a purer Italian, but with the evident intention of keeping him away from the Po valley, where there were too many rumours of revolt.

At Pisa he saw the last embers of the Italian revolution stamped out. It was there that he heard the news of 'fatal Novara' that led to that 'decade of grievous and disillusioned truce' that was for Nievo a period of intense spiritual and artistic ferment. 'The catastrophe of Novara, the downfall of

3

the hopes placed in Pius IX, and later the gallows of Belfiore, seemed to close a cycle of history, nor could any hopes be seen for the morrow.'

In the summer of 1849 he returned to Mantua and later went on to the University of Padua, where he obtained his degree in 1855.

By this time he had already written some books of verse of a fiercely patriotic nature as well as a number of short stories and feuilletons based on the life of the country people of his beloved Friuli. In one of these the description of a requisition by the local police led him into conflict with the Austrian authorities. The charge was of so absurd a nature that even the judges did not take it seriously. None the less, pressure from Vienna assured his conviction and he was sentenced to prison. Nievo appealed, and the case dragged on through court after court, till his sentence was finally and ignominiously commuted for a fine of twenty-five florins. In a letter to a friend Nievo wrote contemptuously: 'To tell you the truth, I felt very little desire to pay and almost preferred to be committed for contempt of court. But it seemed to me that I should have bought martyrdom at too cheap a price.'

His growing political and patriotic enthusiasm, that runs like a scarlet thread through the idyllic prelude and picaresque continuation of the *Confessions*, led him to despise the easygoing manners of his compatriots and he devoted himself to a life of growing austerity and self-discipline. While Austria was preparing fresh political trials and the Mantuans were abandoning themselves to the follies of the carnival, Nievo describes himself in a letter as 'a bull in a group of ballet dancers'.

Meanwhile his family had moved to Udine, and Nievo spent all the time that he could in his beloved Friuli. The countryside, he remarks, strengthens the legs and the mind. 'The Friuli,' he writes, 'is an image of the universe in little. There is no region that includes vistas so various, from the immaculate summits of the Alps to the boundless mirror of the sea, from the marshy plains to the arid mountain ridges where grow the vines.'

4

One of his biographers writes: 'In the Friuli there lived for long the memory of the young poet who strode through the countryside and, if benighted on some country road, would shelter in a peasant's cottage and pass the time with its occupants in telling stories.'

Most of Nievo's early works were published at Udine. All were based on memories of the Friuli and show an interest in, and care for, the peasants that was as refreshing as it was rare in those times. He continually stresses the necessity of getting closer to the country people and, above all, of bringing the literary closer to the popular language, a suggestion also made by Leopardi.

Towards the end of 1857 Nievo had to go to Milan for another hearing of his trial. He remained there, not out of any great affection for that city, but because of his cousin, the Countess Bice Melzi, the great love of his life, whose features and character he immortalized in those of the Pisana. (Her name, however, essentially Venetian, he borrowed from that of another friend, Pisana di Prampero, of San Martino in the Friuli.)

By combining a number of accounts we can get a picture of Nievo at the time when he first met Bice Melzi. Fairly tall, slim and spare, he was dark in complexion, with black hair and very black eyes. His whole being displayed physical vigour, and it was clear to all who came into contact with him that he had grown up in the most perfect balance of body and of spirit. Long experience of the countryside and the open air, rare in Italians of his time and class, had bronzed his skin, hardened his muscles and helped to form his gay and open nature. In life, as in art, he preferred the simplest forms, clear and precise. He never let an opportunity pass of showing his aversion to 'rationalist utopias, declamations and heroic pomposities' or of poking fun at the faint-hearted liberals of his time whom he lampooned as 'penny-a-dozen Robespierres'. He loved to live dangerously but detested shams. When discussing with a friend a project of going to the Balkans to fight the Turks, he begged that his gesture should not be interpreted as a Byronic pose.

5

The *Confessions*, of which *The Castle of Fratta* is the opening part, were written in a fury of creative effort in only eight months, between December 1857 and August 1858, in the midst of patriotic anxieties, amorous distractions and journalistic effort. It remained for some years without a publisher, largely due to the preoccupations of the author, and was only published in 1867, some years after his untimely death. The whole tremendous story at once suggested to Italian critics, as it did later to me in the Castle of Montechiarugolo, a comparison with *War and Peace*, which appeared some two years later. But it seems fairly certain that Tolstoy never saw it.

Written in haste and never revised by the author, the vast canvas of the *Confessions* has many obvious weaknesses. Many parts clearly require the 'labour of the file'. But these criticisms scarcely apply to *The Castle of Fratta*, which is published here with only one short cut in the first few pages—a historical digression of little interest to English readers and which merely slows down the action of the story.

'Even, however, as it has come down to us,' writes a leading Italian critic, 'Nievo's book is one of the greatest and most significant in our literature; ours above all, for its absolute character of *italianità*, which makes it worthy of being compared, alone among Italian novels, to *The Betrothed*. Instead of feigning the rediscovery of ancient chronicles as does Manzoni, or of following the canons of the historical novel as, in their own times, did Guerazzi, d'Azeglio, Cantu and a host of lesser writers, Nievo conceives the artistic daring of imagining himself a man of eighty and recollecting the course of his past life. The man was young, but the artist was already expert enough to be able to merge his thoughts into those of a man of eighty and of contemplating from that serene height all the events of a long and active life; and he relives not only the almost secular existence of a man but with it the life of things and of men, of society and of the family, of institutions and arms, transporting the scene of his novel to the most varied parts of Italy and even abroad.'

*The Castle of Fratta* which opens this vast epic is a story of childhood and of decay; the decay of a feudal society, drawn with swift touches of malignant wit, saved from caricature by his deep feeling for the pitiful and the absurd. The ancient feudal family of Fratta is dying in a shabby aura of magnificence, while in the grass-covered courts and beneath the mouldering towers of its fantastic castle is growing up the new generation that is to supplant it. Even as children, the basic character of the main protagonists becomes clear. Carlo himself, a blend of the author and of his noble grandfather, Carlo Marin; Lucilio, not yet to be seen in the round, but clearly based upon Mazzini himself, and the Pisana: 'Creature of love and ardour, exuberant in fancy, yet in essentials sound, unstable and capricious, yet faithful to a single great love, sinner and heroine, the Pisana is a remarkable woman and certainly among the most original and complete female figures in our literature.'

This assessment is drawn from the full-length Pisana of the whole *Confessions*, yet, as Nievo himself says in *The Castle of Fratta*: 'The Pisana was at that time a little girl, but what are girls but the buds of women? Whether painted in oils or on a miniature the features of a portrait remain ever the same.'

A year after he had laid down the pen and completed the *Confessions*, the young author girded on the sword. The hour had come for that action of which he had himself stressed the necessity. He who had said the first word must complete the last action.

On the 28th of April 1859 the Emperor of Austria declared war on Piedmont. On the 5th of May Nievo crossed the frontier to enlist in the Sardinian army. On the 12th he was enrolled in the Guides and later passed to the mounted 'Cacciatori' of Garibaldi.

On his departure for the front, he commenced another volume of verse, left unfinished, his *Amori Garibaldini*.

Nievo appears to have been an excellent soldier. He took part in many battles, including Varese, San Fermo and the great disillusion of Villafranca. In the reorganization of Garibaldi's armies, Nievo was one of the 'Thousand'.

7

Abba, in his *Noterelle* of Garibaldi's campaigns, writes: 'The Ministry of War is a broken-down cart that follows us, carrying the administration, the maps and the pay chest amounting, as far as we know, to thirty thousand francs. But in this cart we have two treasures: the heart of Acerbi and the intellect of Ippolito Nievo. Nievo is a Venetian poet, who at twenty-eight has written novels, ballads, tragedies. He will be the poet-soldier of our enterprise. I saw him squatting in the bottom of the cart; sharp profile, soft eye, genius shining on his brow . . . a fine soldier.'

Nievo was indeed a fine soldier, though not so enthusiastic about the administrative duties assigned to him. He wanted to live dangerously, to be in the forefront of the battle, and indeed he is reported to have shielded Garibaldi with his own body at the battle of Calatafimi. He intended to become the poet-soldier of the campaigns for, after the entry into Palermo, he added to his *Amori Garibaldini* the first pages of his *Journal of the First Expedition of Sicily*, which also, alas, remained unfinished. However, in the few pages that remain, he has left us a portrait of himself at that time: 'We have the compensation of being regarded as heroes; and this advantage, with a couple of spans of red blouse and seventy centimetres of scimitar, makes us the happiest men on earth. . . . I was dressed as when I left Milan, and carried a huge musket that needed four caps to fire a shot; in compensation I had a loaf of bread spiked on my bayonet, a fine aloe flower in my hat and a magnificent bedcover on my back alla Pollio. I confess that I cut a fine figure! The general [Garibaldi] too was stupendous. He was always in his shirt-sleeves and had the sole advantage over me that his boots, instead of being full of holes, had been repaired . . .'

After the formal wars of over a hundred years, it has been left to men of our own generation to appreciate the vigour, and the valour, of such irregular, partisan, troops.

After the 'Thousand' left Sicily, Nievo was left at Palermo to look after details of the administration. This duty finished, he made a rapid trip to Northern Italy to see Bice Melzi and try to find, in vain, a publisher for the *Confessions*. In February

1861 he was at Naples with the duties of chief of the administration of the Southern Army, when he received orders to go once more to Palermo. By the end of the month, everything was completed and Nievo eager to go. He was advised to leave on the 'Elettrico', the only sound ship then plying between Palermo and the mainland. But the ramshackle 'Ercole' left three days earlier and Ippolito, deaf to the remonstrances of his friends, decided to leave on her.

There were about eighty persons on the 'Ercole' and a certain quantity of military stores. She left Palermo on the 4th of March.

What happened on that voyage is not exactly known. Certainly, the 'Ercole' was never seen again. One version was that the old ship foundered in a violent gale some twenty miles from Capri. The Ministry of War, on the other hand, said that a fire broke out on board during the journey. No wreckage and no bodies were ever found. Nievo perished, his work only just begun. He lost his life trying to anticipate by three days the joy of seeing once again Bice Melzi, whose character and features he has made live for ever in those of the Pisana.

LOVETT F. EDWARDS

# I

I WAS born a Venetian on the 18th of September 1775, the Day of St. Luke the Evangelist, and I shall die, by the Grace of God, an Italian, whenever the Providence that mysteriously controls our world shall so ordain.

That is the lesson of my life. But in so far as this lesson was due not to myself but to the times in which I lived, it has occurred to me that a simple account of the influence of those times upon the life of one man could be of some use to those who, in later days, are destined to feel the less imperfect consequences of what has already been achieved.

In this Year of our Lord 1852 I am now aged more than eighty years, though still young in heart, perhaps more so than in the days of youthful struggle and overtaxed manhood. I have lived and suffered much, but am not less rich in those consolations that, for the most part, remain unrecognized among the tribulations that always owe overmuch to human intolerance and weakness, but none the less uplift the soul to a serenity of peace and hope, when they are recalled to memory as they really were, invincible talismans against every adverse fortune. I mean those feelings and opinions which, even though they are moulded by external events, yet victoriously command them and make of them the fields of active struggle. My nature, my talent, my early education and the progress of my destiny were, as all things human, a mingling of good and of bad; were it not an indiscreet quirk of modesty I could also add that, in my own case, the bad was rather more abundant than the good.

Nothing of all this would be unusual or worth the telling, were it not that my life was passed astride those two centuries which will always remain a memorable epoch, more especially in the history of Italy. Then could be seen the first ripening of the fruit of those political speculations that from the fourteenth to the eighteenth centuries were evident in the works of Dante, of Machiavelli, of Filicaia, of Vico and of so many others whose names my mediocre culture and almost complete literary ignorance can no longer recall. The chance, some might say the mischance, of having lived in those years has therefore led me to this task of writing what I have seen, felt, done and experienced from early childhood to the advent of old age, when the infirmities of age, forbearance to those younger, the temperance of mature opinions and, let me say also, the experience of many misfortunes in these recent years, have driven me to this country dwelling whence I have taken part in the last and most ridiculous episode of the great feudal drama. Nor has my simple account any more importance to history than would be a note added by an unknown but contemporary hand to the revelations of an ancient codex. The private activities of a man who was neither so petty as to withdraw himself from the common miseries, nor so stoical as to oppose them deliberately, nor indeed so wise or so proud as to pass them by disdainfully, should, it seems to me, in some way reflect the communal and national activity that absorbed them, even as the fall of a drop of water indicates the direction of the rain.

Thus an account of my experiences will serve as an example of those countless individual destinies that, from the breaking up of the old political orders to the refashioning of the present one, together compose the great national destiny of Italy. Perhaps I deceive myself, but I feel that, in thinking them over, some young men may be able to avoid being disheartened by dangerous allurements and others filled with enthusiasm for the work so slowly but lastingly accomplished, while many may be able to fix securely those wayward aspirations that lead them to try a hundred ways before finding that one which leads them into the true practice of civil ministry. So at least it has appeared to me in the nine years which, by fits and starts and as memory and inspiration have suggested, I have spent in writing these notes. I began them with unwavering faith on the eve of a great defeat and brought them to an end through a long expiation in these years of renewed effort, and they have in some measure helped to persuade me of the greater energy and more legitimate hopes of the present in comparison with the spectacle of the weaknesses and wickednesses of the past.

And now, before setting down to transcribe them, I have wished, in these few lines of prelude, to define and better to justify that idea that has led me, in my old age and without literary art, to try, perhaps in vain, to learn the difficult art of writing. Let the clarity of ideas, the simplicity of sentiments and the truth of history be my excuse and a compensation for my lack of rhetoric. The sympathy of kind readers rather than the desire of reputation will sustain me.

In the shadow of the tomb, already long alone in the world, abandoned both by friends and enemies, without fears and without hopes that are not of eternity, freed by age from those passions which only too often caused my judgements to deviate from the true path, and from the transient hopes of my not overbold ambition, I have garnered in my life one fruit alone, peace of soul. In this I live content, in this I place my trust; this I hand on to my younger brothers as the most enviable of treasures, as the unique shield to defend one against the lure of false friends, the deceptions of the vile and the extravagances of the powerful. Yet one more thing I must say, a thing to which the experience of an octogenarian may perhaps add some authority, and that is, that life as I experienced it was on the whole good, whenever humility allows us to consider ourselves merely the infinitesimal creations of human life, and whenever uprightness of soul accustoms us to look on the good of others as in great measure superior to the good of ourselves alone.

My earthly existence at last is coming to its end; content with the good that I have done and sure that I have repaired, as far as in me lies, the evil that I have committed, I have no other hope and no other faith save to flow into and become one with the great sea of existence. The peace that I now enjoy is like that mysterious gulf at the end of which the bold navigator finds a passage to the infinite calm of the Ocean of Eternity. But my thought, before plunging into that time when time exists no more, leaps forward once again into the future of men; to them I confidently bequeath my own faults to be

13

discerned, my own hopes to be collected, my own vows to be accomplished.

I passed my early years in the Castle of Fratta, which is now no more than a heap of ruins whence the peasants take at their pleasure stones and rubble for draining the subsoil of their mulberry trees. But at that time it was a huge block of buildings with towers and pepper-pots, a great drawbridge rickety with age, and the finest Gothic windows to be found between the Lemene and the Tagliamento. In all my travels I have never encountered any buildings that made so bizarre a spectacle on the landscape, nor which had angles, cornices, embrasures and bastions sufficient to content all the quarters and sub-quarters of the wind-rose.* These angles were combined with such daring fantasy that there was not one that matched its companion. I do not know whether or not the T-square had ever been used in their construction, or whether all those that lumber up the studios of engineers had become exhausted in the process.

The castle stood firmly between extremely deep moats where sheep pastured whenever the frogs were not croaking there; but the slow growth of the ivy had gradually invested it by the counterscarps and, sprouting here and climbing there, had finished by creating such draperies of festoons and arabesques that the reddish colour of the stone could no longer be seen. Nobody ever dreamed of laying a hand upon this venerable covering of the ancient signorial dwelling, and even the shutters torn down by the north wind hardly dared to break off some hanging fringe. Another anomaly of this building was the multitude of chimneys, which from a distance gave it the appearance of a chess-board spread with a still unfinished game. Certain it is that if its ancient lords could have counted one retainer per chimney it would have been the best guarded castle of all Christendom.

Its high portalled courtyards, filled with mud and hen-roosts, fulfilled with their internal disorder the promise of the façade,

* The 'compass' showing prevailing winds on old maps.

14

even the campanile of the chapel was cracked here and there by the repeated salutations of the lightning. But its perseverance was in some way justified, since there never howled a *temporale* that its cracked bell did not make welcome, so it became almost a duty to return the courtesy with a thunderbolt or two. Some gave the merit of these meteorological jests to the age-old poplars that shaded the countryside around the castle, while the peasants said that, since the devil inhabited it, it was natural that from time to time it should be visited by some of his good companions. The gentry, used to seeing only the campanile struck, were accustomed to regard it as a sort of lightning rod and willingly abandoned it to the celestial anger, if only thereby the roofs of the barns and the great cowl of the kitchen chimney remained unharmed.

But we have now reached a point which requires a fairly long digression. Suffice it to say that, for me who have not seen either the Colossus of Rhodes or the Pyramids of Egypt, the kitchen of Fratta and its hearth were the most awe-inspiring monuments that ever burdened the surface of the earth. The Cathedral of Milan and the Temple of St. Peter are indeed something, but they do not by a long way give an equal impression of immensity and solidity. Nothing similar can I recollect ever having seen save Hadrian's Mole, although since it has been transformed into the Castel Sant Angelo it seems to-day much diminished.

The kitchen of Fratta was a vast place, with an indefinite number of walls very varied in size, which rose towards the heavens like a cupola and delved under the earth deeper than an abyss; obscure, even black, with a secular layer of soot, whence shone like so many huge diabolical eyes the shining bottoms of saucepans, dripping pans and flasks, cumbered in every direction with immense sideboards, colossal dressers and endless tables, it was haunted at all hours of the day or night with an unknown quantity of black and grey cats, which gave it the appearance of a witches' laboratory—so much for the kitchen. But in the deepest and darkest of its chasms yawned an acherontic gulf, a cavern still more grim and terrifying,

15

where the darkness was broken by the crackling flicker of embers and the greenish light of two window-slits with double iron grilles. There, there was a dense curling of smoke, an eternal bubbling of beans in monstrous cauldrons. There, sitting in rows on creaking and smoke-blackened benches, was a grave sanhedrin of fateful and somnolent figures. This was the hearth and the domestic Curia of the castellans of Fratta. But hardly had the evening Ave Maria sounded and the echo of the Angelus Domini ceased, than the scene changed in a moment and for that little world of shadows commenced the hours of light. The old cook lit four lamps with a single taper, two under the chimney shaft of the hearth and one on either side of the Madonna of Loreto. Then she dragged together the embers with an enormous poker and threw on them an armful of thorns and juniper. The lamps reflected a calm yellowish light, the fire crackled into smoke which rose in curling spirals right up to the crossbar of the two gigantic andirons bossed with bronze, and the evening inhabitants of the kitchen revealed their varied faces to the light.

The Count of Fratta was a man of more than sixty, who seemed as if he had just that moment stepped out of his armour, so rigid and pokerlike he sat in his great armchair. But his wig, his purse, his ash-coloured surcoat piped with scarlet and the boxwood snuffbox always in his hands were a trifle out of keeping with this military attitude. It is true that he held between his legs a slender sword, but its sheath was so rusty that it could well have been exchanged for one of the spits and, furthermore, I could not assure you that there was really a steel blade concealed in that sheath, and the Count himself had probably never taken the trouble to convince himself of the fact.

The Count was always shaved with such care that he looked as if he had just come from the hands of the barber; from morn till eve he always carried a blue kerchief under his armpit and, though he seldom went out on foot and never on horseback, he wore jackboots and spurs that would not have disgraced a courtier of Frederick II. This was a tacit declaration of

16

sympathy with the Prussian party, and though the wars in Germany had long been over, he had not ceased to menace the imperial faction with the disfavour of his spurs.

When the Count spoke, everyone agreed with him, either aloud or with a nod of the head; when he laughed, everyone hastened to laugh too; when he sneezed after snuff, eight or nine voices competed with: 'Long live the Count', 'Good health' or 'God preserve the Signor Count'; and when he rose, all rose. When he left the kitchen, all, even including the cats, breathed deeply with both lungs as if a millstone had been taken from their chests. But more profoundly than all the rest breathed the Chancellor, if the Count did not make a sign to him to follow, and mercifully permitted him to remain in the quiet ease of the hearth. It must, however, be added that this miracle occurred but seldom. They rose together and sat together, and their legs alternated in so true a measure that they seemed to be keeping time with the beating of drums. When these habits were first being formed, the frequent desertions of his shadow had made the Count turn around every three paces to see if he were being followed according to his desire. But by now the Chancellor had become resigned to his destiny, and occupied the second half of his day in picking up his patron's kerchief, wishing him good health at every sneeze, approving his every observation and telling him whatever he felt would be received with favour in all matters concerning the local administration of justice. For example, if a peasant accused of stealing the first-fruits of the signorial garden replied to the reprimands of the Chancellor by flattering him or perhaps by slipping a half-ducat into his hand, the Chancellor would tell the magistrate that such and such a one, terrified by the severe justice of His Excellency, had asked for mercy, had repented of his misdeeds and was disposed to make amends with whatever fine might be considered adequate. The Count then breathed in enough air to have sustained Goliath for a week and replied that the clemency of Titus should be mingled with the justice of the tribunals and that he for his part would pardon anyone who genuinely repented.

17

The Chancellor, perhaps for modesty s sake, was as humble and disorderly in his appearance as his principal was pompous and splendid. But nature had counselled him to such modesty, since a more miserable and afflicted manikin it would have been hard to find. It was sometimes said that he squinted as a matter of habit; but the fact was that few squinters had as much right to the title as he. His nose, aquiline, hooked and snub at the same time, was a Gordian knot of noses aborted together; and his mouth yawned beneath it so menacingly that the poor nose used to draw itself up for fear of falling into it. His legs, gaitered in leather, were splayed out on either side of him to give the maximum support to a figure which it seemed must collapse before every puff of wind. Without wishing to joke, I believe that if you had taken away the wig, the clothes and the sword, the weight of the Chancellor of Fratta would not have surpassed a bare twenty pounds, counting therein for a full four the goitre which he sought to hide behind an immense starched ruff. Ugly as he was, he had the happy illusion of thinking himself anything but unappetizing and he would talk on no subject so willingly as on beautiful women and gallantry.

How content Madame Justice was to find herself in his hands I could not in all conscience tell you. But I remember to have seen more downcast than contented faces descend the open staircase of the Chancellery. There was much trumpeting in his anteroom on audience days, and those who had big fists and loud voices and used them alternately, and who in addition had silver in their pockets, easily obtained the fruits of justice before his tribunal. What I can say is that on two occasions I happened to witness floggings in the courtyard of the castle, and on both occasions this ceremony involved two poor devils who certainly had not deserved it. It was well for them that the Serjeant empowered with the execution of justice high and low was a man of judgement and wielded the rope's end with such skill that the weals healed at the worst on the seventh day. Therefore Marchetto, nicknamed the Bonebreaker, was as loved by the common people as the Chancellor was hated. As

18

for the Count, concealed as was Destiny in ancient times in the high clouds of Olympus, he escaped both the hatred and the love of his vassals. They took off their hats to him as to the image of some foreign saint in whom they had small confidence, and drove their carts into the ditch when the postillion on the roof of his bombay shouted to them to make way while still a good half mile distant.

The Count had a brother who in no way resembled him and was an honorary canon of the Cathedral at Portogruaro, the roundest, smoothest and most mellifluous canon in the whole diocese, a real man of peace who divided his time wisely between the breviary and the table without letting his greater predilection for the one or for the other be revealed. Monsignor Orlando was not begotten by milord his father with any idea of dedicating him to Mother Church; his baptismal name was witness for this. The genealogical tree of the Counts of Fratta had always boasted some military glory in every generation, and he had been destined to perpetuate the family tradition. But man proposes and God disposes; this time at least the great proverb was not wrong. The future General began his life by demonstrating an extraordinary affection for his wet-nurse, so that it was not possible to wean him before the age of two. Even at that time it was still uncertain whether the one word he could utter was 'pap' or 'papa'.

When he was at last able to walk, they began putting wooden swords and cardboard helmets in his hands; but hardly had they done so before he escaped into the chapel to play with the sacristan's broom. As for trying to accustom him to real weapons, he showed from the first an instinctive revulsion against table knives and wanted at all costs to cut his meat up with a spoon. His father tried to vanquish this accursed repugnance by making him sit on the knee of one of his buli (feudal retainers); but the little Orlando was so terrified that they had to transfer him to the cook's lap lest he should die of fright. After the wet-nurse, the cook was his second love; it was not for nothing that he made clear his vocation. The Chancellor held that the captains of old time always ate so much

19

that the little master would indeed in course of time become a famous captain.

The old Count was not reassured by these hopes, and sighed as his eyes wandered from the puffy and bewildered face of his second-born to the proud and hirsute moustachios of the old family portraits. He had dedicated the last powers of his generative faculties to the ambitious task of inscribing in the future annals of the family a Grand Master of the Order of Malta or an Admiral of the Most Serene Republic, and it galled him to have employed them merely to have at his table the terrific appetite of a Captain of the Cernide (local militia). Therefore he redoubled his zeal to awaken and stir up the bellicose spirit of Orlando; but the effect did not justify his efforts. Orlando built little altars in every corner of the castle, sang Mass, high, low and ceremonial, with the sacristan's brats and whenever he saw a musket, flattened himself under one of the kitchen sideboards. Then they tried other means of persuasion, forbidding him to play in the sacristy and to sing vespers through his nose as he had heard the choirboys of the parish do. But his mother was scandalized by such violence and began, on her side, secretly to take up the defence of her son. Orlando found it much to his taste to act the part of a little martyr; and since his mother's sweetmeats amply consoled him for his father's rebuffs, the profession of priest seemed to him more than ever preferable to that of a soldier. The cook and the house-servants sniffed around him an odour of sanctity and thenceforward he began to grow fat with contentment and to show an even more exaggerated devotion in order to maintain the adoration of the womenfolk. So that finally his august father, with his military ambitions, had against him the opinion of the whole family. Even the buli, who always supported the cook's party when their feudal master was out of hearing, deplored the sacrilege of obstinately trying to turn a St. Louis from the true path. But the feudal master was obstinate and only after twelve years of vain assault decided to lift the siege and to put away in the storehouse of vanished dreams the future military laurels of Orlando. One fine morning Orlando

20

was called with imposing solemnity before his father who, however much he outwardly assumed the authoritative frown of the absolute master, yet felt within him the vacillating and contrite feelings of a general about to capitulate.

'My son,' he began, 'the profession of arms is a noble profession.'

'So I believe,' replied the boy with a saintly expression, a little marred by a sly glance secretly directed towards his mother.

'You bear a proud name,' continued the old Count, sighing, 'Orlando, as you must have learnt from the poem of Ariosto which I have so much recommended you to study . . .'

'I read the Offices of the Madonna,' interrupted the boy, humbly.

'Excellent,' continued the old man, adjusting the wig on his forehead, 'but Ariosto is also worthy of being read. Orlando was a great paladin who liberated from the Moors the fair realm of France. And even more, if you have glanced through *Gerusalemme Liberata*, you would know that it was not with the Offices of the Madonna, but with great strokes of the sword and thrusts of the lance that the good Geoffrey wrested from the hands of the Saracens the Sepulchre of Christ.'

'May God be praised,' exclaimed the boy. 'Then there remains nothing more to be done!'

'Nothing more, indeed!' burst out the old man. 'Know then, wretched boy, that the infidels reconquered the Holy Land and that now, even as we are speaking, a Pasha of the Sultan governs Jerusalem to the shame of all Christendom!'

'I will pray the Good Lord that such shame should cease,' put in Orlando.

'Prayers, indeed! It is deeds that are needed,' shouted the old Count.

'Your pardon,' interrupted the Countess, 'but you surely do not pretend that our baby should carry out a crusade all by himself.'

'Bah! He is no longer a baby,' replied the Count. 'He has just completed his twelfth year.'

21

'Even had he completed his hundredth,' went on the Countess, 'it is certainly not necessary to fill his head with the conquest of Palestine.'

'We shall never conquer it as long as we teach our children to play the woman with a rosary,' exclaimed the old man, purple with anger.

'It only wanted that sort of blasphemy!' the Countess went on patiently. 'Since the Good Lord has granted us a son who has the idea of being good, let us show ourselves grateful indeed by refusing to recognize his gifts!'

'Fine gifts, fine gifts!' muttered the Count, ' . . . a gluttonous little saintling . . . half fox and half rabbit . . .'

'At least he never said anything like that,' added the lady. 'All he said was that he would pray to God to grant that the places of His passion and His death return to the hands of the Christians. That is the best thing to do now, since the Christians of to-day are occupied in cutting one another's throats and the profession of soldier has become a mere school of cutthroats and butchers.'

'Body of the Serenissima!' thundered the Count. 'If Sparta had had mothers like you, Xerxes would have passed Thermopylae with three hundred hogsheads.'

'Even had things been as you say, I should not have worried overmuch,' replied the Countess.

'What!' roared the old man. 'Have you reached the point of denying even the heroism of Leonidas and the virtue of the Spartan mothers?'

'Bah! Now we know where we are,' the lady said quietly. 'I know little enough of Leonidas and the Spartan mothers, though I have heard them mentioned only too often; furthermore, I am quite prepared to believe blindly that they were very fine fellows. But recall that we have summoned before us our son Orlando to throw some light on his true vocation and not to squabble in his presence about these rancid fairytales.'

'Women, women! . . . Born to educate hens!' muttered the Count.

'Husband mine! I am a Badoera!' said the Countess, drawing herself up. 'You will allow, I hope, that the hens in my family are not more numerous than the capons in yours!'

Orlando, who had been holding his sides for some time past, now broke into a laugh at this fine compliment of Madame his mother but was quelled instantly like a wet chicken at the severe glance she turned on him.

'You see,' she went on, speaking to her husband, 'we will end up by losing both goat and cabbages. Put a rein on your caprices till God makes you understand He cannot be thwarted for nothing, and ask yourself instead, as becomes a good father of a family, about the soul of this boy.'

The old impenitent bit his lip and turned to his son with an expression on his face so terrifying that the boy was scared out of his wits and ran to hide his head in his mother's lap.

'So,' the old Count began, without looking at him, since he felt that if he did so his anger would rise again. 'So, my son, you do not want to make your appearance on a fine horse, with trappings of gold and red velvet, with a long flaming sword in your hand and behind you six regiments of Slavs, all six feet high, who only wait an order from you to rush to their death on the Turkish scimitars?'

'I want to sing Masses, I do!' whimpered the boy from under his mother's apron.

The Count, hearing this whining voice half suffocated by the folds of the garment whence it issued, turned to see what was the matter, and seeing his son with his head wrapped up like a pheasant in its hide, could no longer control his anger.

'Go to the seminary then, bastard!' he shouted, rushing out of the room.

The little wretch began to sob and tear his hair and beat his head against his mother's lap, quite sure that he could not do himself any harm. But she took him in her arms and consoled him with caresses, saying:

'Yes, heart of mine, don't be afraid; we will make a priest of you. You will sing Mass. You are not made, indeed, to spill the blood of your brothers like Cain.'

23

'Ee, ee, ee! I want to sing in the choir! I want to become a saint!' howled.Orlando.

'Yes, yes . . . you will sing in the choir; we shall make a canon of you. You shall have your cloak and your fine red stockings. Don't cry, my treasure. These are trials which we must bear for the Good Lord's sake, to make ourselves more worthy of him,' went on his mother.

The boy consoled himself with these promises, and therefore the Count Orlando, despite his baptismal name, and in opposition to his father's views, became Monsignor Orlando. But however much the Curia was disposed to favour the devout ambition of the Countess, none the less, Orlando was no eagle, so that it took no less than twelve years in the seminary and another thirty as a postulant to help him to reach even the half of his aspirations; and the Count had the triumph, and the Countess the mortification, of dying many years before the red flakes began to snow down upon his head. None the less, it could not be said that our priest entirely wasted all this time of waiting. He acquired a respectable knowledge of the missal; and his shirt-front developed to such an extent that it would rival the softest and most elaborate of any of his colleagues.

A castle which sheltered within its walls two such dignitaries, forensic and clerical, as the Chancellor and Monsignor Orlando, could not be without its military celebrity also. The Captain Sandracca wanted to be a Slav at all costs, though it was rumoured that he had been born at Ponte di Piave. Certainly he was the tallest man in the whole neighbourhood and the goddesses of grace and beauty had not presided at his birth. But none the less he spent a good hour every day in making himself three times as ugly as he was already and was always studying some new way of glowering or some new embellishment of his moustaches to make himself still more formidable.

To listen to him when he had emptied his fourth glass, there was no war from the siege of Troy to that of Belgrade where he had not fought like a lion. But once the fumes of the wine had a little chilled, his pretensions were reduced to more honest proportions. He contented himself then with recounting how he had received twelve wounds in the war of Candia, offering on every occasion to take down his breeches and let you count them. And God alone knew how these wounds could have been made, since now, on thinking it over, it does not appear to me likely that, with the fifty years which he then admitted to, he could have taken part in a war fought sixty years before. Perhaps his memory deceived him and made him believe the exploits of some braggart which he had heard recounted by the storytellers of the Piazza San Marco to be his own. Indeed, the good Captain got confused easily enough with his dates. But he never forgot the first of each month to make sure he was paid by the factor his twenty ducats of salary as Captain of the Cernide (militia). That day was his festa.

At crack of dawn he sent out two drummers who hammered away until noon in all the four cantons of the jurisdiction. Then, in the afternoon, when the militia was assembled in the courtyard of the castle, he would come out of his room looking so ugly, so very ugly, that his appearance alone was enough to throw his little army into confusion. He wielded a great sword, so long that it would have sufficed to mark the pace of an entire column. And since at the slightest mistake he used mercilessly to beat with it the paunches of the front rank, as soon as he appeared to lower it the front rank withdrew upon the second, the second upon the third, and thus created such confusion that the approach of the Turkish army itself could not have caused more. The Captain smiled with content and reassembled his troop, raising his sword. Then those twenty or thirty ragged peasants, with their muskets over their shoulders like so many mattocks, recommenced their march towards the square, to the beating of drums. But as the Captain marched ahead on legs so much longer than the longest in his company, he always arrived alone upon the square. Then he would turn furiously to rain blows upon this indolent rabble; but none of them was stupid enough to await them. Some took to their heels, others leapt over ditches, others squeezed behind doors and others hid in the hayricks. The drummers defended themselves with their drums. So almost always ended the monthly review of the militia in the jurisdiction of Fratta. The Captain sent in a long report, the Chancellor put it in the archives and nothing more was said on the subject until the next month.

It may seem very remarkable to read to-day of such political and military goings-on, which appear to be mere buffoonery. But matters were exactly as I have described. The district of Portogruaro, to which the commune of Teglio, which included the parish of Fratta, belonged, now forms the eastern march of the Venetian Province, which covers the whole plain from the lower Adige in the Polesine and the steep banks of the Taglia- mento down to the edge of the lagoons. In the time of which I write, matters remained as nature had made them and Attila had left them. The Friuli obeyed some sixty or seventy families, by origin from across the Alps but assimilated in the country by a century-old residence, to whom was entrusted local and absolute authority in the jurisdiction of their several dominions; and their votes, with those of the Free Communes and the Counties, formed the Parliament of the Fatherland that met once every year as a consultative body in association with the Viceroy sent to Udine from Venice.

I have few sins of omission upon my conscience, but amongst them the most serious and the one that causes me the most regret is that I was never present at one of these Parlia- ments. To have been there must really have been a most en- tertaining experience. Few of the Magistrates knew how to read; and the deputies of the countryside can hardly have known more than they. That all understood Tuscan I do not believe; that none spoke it is sufficiently shown by their de- crees and the resolutions adopted, wherein, after a short pre- amble in Latin, they rushed headlong into a mishmash of Italian, Friuli and Venetian that was not without its beauty for those who liked a good laugh. Everything therefore combined to assure that when the Magnificent General Parliament of the Fatherland petitioned His Serenity the Doge for leave to legis- late upon a given subject, the tenor of those laws should already

26

have been concerted down to the smallest detail between His Excellency the Viceroy and the Most Excellent Council of Ten. The fact was that, once permission had been obtained to make suggestions on any given matter, the Magnificent General Parliament proposed, discussed and approved everything in a single day, more precisely on the 11th of August. The reason for this haste and for the choice of this, rather than any other day, was that precisely at this time the Fair of Saint Lorenzo was held, which afforded an opportunity for all the members of the Parliament to meet at Udine. But since, during the Fair, few had any inclination to neglect their own affairs for those of the public, the period of twenty-four hours was considered amply sufficient to relieve them of the latter cares. The Magnificent General Parliament then implored the dominant Most Serene Republic for confirmation of all that had been discussed, proposed and approved; and once this confirmation had been received, the town crier announced to all and sundry, to the sound of the trumpet, on the feast day, all the resolutions taken by the Magnificent General Parliament. It did not follow that all the laws promulgated by this method must therefore have been unjust or ridiculous; since, as says the editor of the Friulian Statutes, 'these laws are an embodiment of justice, maturity and experience and have always in view commendable and salutary objects'; but there might well be considerable doubt about the merit which the magnificent deputies of the Fatherland could claim for themselves.

One amongst their many laws that merits especial praise is that of 1770 which occupied itself with the reorganization of the Cernide, or local militia, raised by the communes and the Feudal Lords to maintain order in their respective jurisdictions. 'The Signor Syndics and Inquisitors hereby permit the Cernide, the Corporals and the Heads of Hundreds (Captain Sandracca was a Head of a Hundred, or perhaps fifty or twenty according to the good will of his subalterns, but arrogated to himself the title of Captain in view of his past glories), permit them, I repeat, to carry freely their muskets unloaded in the cities and cultivated areas while in transit or on duty, but never in church, at feasts or markets or while accompanying citizens.' 'They can furthermore'—thus the Most Illustrious Syndics—'on occasions of parades, reviews, inspections and patrols, be armed other than with firearms with a bayonet; but with entire prohibition of the dagger, forbidden also in the territory of the old republic, but now also applied to the impudent use of knives, arms that are abominable to all classes of militia and condemned by all the laws.'

This paragraph affected, more than the Cernide, the insolent castellans who used to recruit the famous buli, who were armed to the teeth, and whom they kept as retainers for their usual exactions. It is, however, right to add, in praise of the Counts of Fratta, that their buli were famous in the whole area for an exemplary meekness and that they kept them more out of custom than for any kind of arrogance.

Captain Sandracca, the ancient hero of Candia, looked with horror upon this rabble of vagabonds, as he used to term them, and had so influenced the Count that he had relegated them to a tiny room close to the stables while Marchetto, the serjeant, who on occasion was their leader, was not allowed to enter the kitchen without first leaving his pistol and his knife in the entry. As a reason for this horror of knives, the Captain gave the same motive as the Syndics, namely that such arms are abominable to all types of militia. He said, moreover, that he was more afraid of a knife than of a cannon; and this may well have been true at Fratta where a cannon had never yet been seen.

But the control of arms was no easy matter in a province divided and subdivided into a hundred different authorities, superimposed and interdependent, and with common frontiers with many foreign countries such as the Tyrol and the County of Gorizia, and furrowed at every step with rivers and torrents whereon not merely bridges but even ferries were very rare, and made ten times larger than it is to-day by roads badly made, deep in mud, infamous to a degree and more likely to hinder than to assist travellers. I can remember that, up to twenty years ago, to go from Colloredo to Collalto, a distance

28

of four miles, two mettlesome and powerful horses sweated for three hours to drag any coach sufficiently well made to withstand the lurches due to the holes and rocks that it encountered. More than that, there was a good mile where the road ran in a ditch or torrent; and to overcome this, the assistance of a pair of bullocks was considered indispensable. The carriage roads in the rest of the province were no better, and anyone can work out for himself what must have been the executive power of the authorities over persons assisted on every side with so many natural obstacles.

Amongst such obstacles I would like to be able to omit the idleness and venal complicity of the officials, the serjeants and even the Chancellors, who were almost compelled to such compromises to remedy the excessive moderation of the tariffs and the proverbial avarice of their principals. There were some, for example, who instead of rewarding their Chancellors or notaries with a sufficient wage, aimed at sharing with them the dues they collected, and I can recall one such notary who was compelled to condemn persons to twice what should have been due in order to satisfy the greed of the magistrate and, at the same time, extract from them something on which to live himself. Another castellan, when he was hard up, used to denounce himself to his own Chancellery for some imagined crime in order to pocket his share of the charges due to the official over the trial of the person condemned.

The Magistrate and the Chancellor of Fratta were not of such sentiments; but I none the less cannot recall ever having heard their justice exalted to the skies. Instead, the Chancellor, whenever he was relieved of his ministry as shadow to the Signor Count and was not wasting his time chattering about loose ladies and gay intrigues, would break into interminable laments about the meanness of the legal tariffs, which, according to him, absolutely prohibited the entry into Paradise of any officer of justice who could not prove categorically to St. Peter that he had died of hunger. With what right he complained, I do not wish to judge; I know, however, that the investigation of one or more culprits was rewarded according to

29

the tariff by one lire, equivalent to fifty centisimi of stamp duty. I believe it would not be possible to assure justice to the citizens at a cheaper rate; but it is with justice as it is with other things, that he who spends more spends less; and proverbs are seldom wrong.

It was the same thing with letters, where the postal charges within the borders of Fratta were three soldi a letter. But delivery was a mere matter of chance with those infernal roads; and what did so cheap a charge serve when one had to write ten letters in order to assure the arrival of one and even that one only arrived by chance and in many cases was quite useless because of the delay?

Certainly, for those who had inherited many rights and few duties, and intended to continue their usage, St. Mark was a most commendable master. No conservative was more conservative than he, not even Metternich or Chateaubriand. As the Friuli had at one time been attached to the Patriarchs of Aquileia, it had kept its jurisdictions, its statutes and its Parliaments. Phantasms of public life, they perhaps harboured a germ of vitality, but under the wings of the Lion they finally did no more than to conceal a profound indifference, or a tired resignation to the old-fashioned ordinances of the Republic. The casual forays of the Turks towards the end of the fifteenth century had imbued this frontier province of Italy with an immeasurable, almost superstitious, fear; so that its present attachment to Venice, as the old-time victor over the Ottoman power, seemed a stroke of good fortune. But the astute old trader knew that to maintain her power without force in this new dominion, she had need of the strong arms of the castellans, now risen to a height of insolent power after the need that the countryside had had for them during the last invasions of the Turks. Hence the tolerance of the old feudal ordinances; which were perpetuated, even as everything was perpetuated in the body, crumbling and already weakened, of the Republic.

The nobles went on living in castles three centuries after their colleagues and compatriots elsewhere had already become citizens, and the virtues of ancient times had already in

30

part become vices, as the general change of conditions took from them the air in which they breathed. Valour became ferocity, pride became arrogance, and hospitality changed little by little into a proud and illegal protection of the worst types of gallows birds. St. Mark drowsed; and, when he watched and punished, his justice was done in darkness, atrocious in its mystery and useless as an example.

Meanwhile, the Friuli patricians began to split into two factions; the one peasant, rough, wild and little propitious to the domination of the Venetian curias; the other Venetianized, town-dwelling, softened by long consorting with the nobles of the Dominant City. Ancient family traditions and the proximity of the lands of the Empire drew the former to the Imperial party; the latter, by similarity of customs, turned to a sheeplike obedience to their rulers; rebels the first by instinct, sheeplike the second by worthlessness, both were more than useless, indeed were harmful, to the good of their country. Thus one could see many patrician houses in the service of the Court of Vienna for many generations, while others, allied by kinship with the nobles of the Canalazzo, were honoured in the Republic by exalted positions. But the two parties had divided between them the customs and the favours in a somewhat promiscuous manner. Thus some amongst the most turbulent castellans were sometimes seen to go to Venice to make amends for their misdeeds and to buy forgetfulness from the senators with long purses of zecchini. There were also some petty lords, Venetianized in the city for the three months of winter, who, once returned behind their own battlements, became more ferocious than ever, though their bragging often seemed more knavery than violence, and even before committing their misdemeanours they had usually assured impunity for their actions.

As for justice, it was a cat and dog affair, that is, none considered it seriously save for a few timorous Godfearers who used to blunder into punishment through ignorance. This was the kingdom of knaves; and it was only with knavery that the common people could find the way to recompense themselves

31

for the arrogances that they suffered. In the forensic transactions of the Friuli the astuteness of the administered took the place of the *equitas* of the Roman law, while the greed and pride of the officials and their patrons marked the limits of the *strictum jus*.

Howsoever it was, it chanced that on this side of the Tagliamento the castellans were largely of the Venetian party, to which the Counts of Fratta boasted that they had belonged from time immemorial; whilst on the other side the Imperial faction lorded it openly; the former were the more popular and the richer, the latter far superior in activity and audacity. However, even amongst these there were some who blew now hot now cold and some who remained lukewarm and these last always among the most useless and the worst. The summary justice executed by the Council of Ten on occasional imprudent ones accused of conspiring in favour of the imperialists and to the detriment of the Republic, was not of a sort to encourage the plots of the seditious. But such outbreaks were too rare for the terror of them to endure for long, and the plots continued more and more frivolous and innocuous as the times became unpropitious and the common people indifferent to these artificial and unsought innovations.

In the days of Maria Theresa three castellans of the Piedemonte, a Franzi, a Tarcentini and a Partistagno, were accused of stirring up unrest and of trying to influence the country in favour of the Empress. The Council of Ten spied on them carefully and it might well have been that the accusations were not false. More than all the rest, the Partistagno, with his castle almost on the Illyrian frontier, took open part for the imperialists, mocked at St. Mark and at the head of his long table drank to the day when the Signor Viceroy—I repeat the words of his toast—and all the other *caca in aqua* would be kicked in the pants to the other side of the Tagliamento. Everyone laughed at these fine words and the boldness of the feudal lord was admired and even imitated, as far as they dared, by the vassals and castellans of the neighbourhood. At Venice a Secret Council was held and it was decided that these three

32

turbulent lords should be cited to appear in Venice to justify themselves; everyone knew that such justification was the surest step to the famous prison of 'The Leads'.

The redoubtable Messer Grande was therefore sent to the Friuli with three sealed letters, each of which was to be unsealed and read in the presence of the respective culprit, and which contained the order to come in person to Venice to reply to the questions of the Most Excellent Council of Ten. Such injunctions were usually blindly obeyed; the power of the Lion still appeared so formidable to those distant and ignorant that it was considered useless to try to escape it. Messer Grande therefore came in solemn embassy to the Franzi and the Tarcentini, both of whom bowed their heads and went voluntarily to put themselves in the dungeons of the Inquisitors. Thence he passed with the third letter to the castle of the Partistagno, who had already heard of the submission of his companions and awaited him respectfully in the great hall of his castle. Messer Grande entered with his great red robe sweeping up the dust and with due solemnity drew the letter from his breast and began to read the contents. He read with a nasal voice 'that the noble and exalted Signor Gherardo di Partistagno should be requested within seven days to present himself before the Most Excellent Council of Ten, etc., etc.' The noble and exalted Signor Gherardo di Partistagno stood before him, trembling and with bowed head, as if listening to a sentence of death. At the sight of this attitude of submission, the voice of Messer Grande became ever more menacing and finally, when he read the signatures, it seemed that through his nostrils breathed all the terrors of the Inquisitorial Council. The Partistagno with trembling voice assured him that he would incontinently obey and made a sign with the hand which had been supporting him on a table, as if to command a horse or a litter. Messer Grande, proud of having fulminated according to his usual custom against the proud feudatory, turned on his heel to leave the hall, head erect. But he had not moved a step before seven or eight buli, brought specially the day before from a castle of the Partistagno in Illyria, leapt on him and striking him here and

33

pounding him there, gave him such a beating that in a very short time poor Messer Grande had not enough breath in his body to shout. The Partistagno encouraged the scoundrels, shouting:

'Yes, indeed! I am ready to obey. Give it him hot, Natale! Down, down with this parchment nose! To dare to come here, to my own castle, with such a message! Clever, indeed! A rogue, by Diana. . . . What a state you are in, Messer! Bravo, my sons! Now, enough, enough; give him breath enough to get back to Venice to tell the news to these good signors. . . .'

'Ay, ay, treason! mercy! I am dead!' groaned Messer Grande, quivering on the floor and trying to put himself to rights.

'No, you are not dead,' replied the Partistagno. 'You see? . . . You can still stand well enough, and with a little mending of your fine red clothes there won't be a sign of this unpleasant incident to be seen. Now go. . . .' So saying, he led him to the door of the hall. 'Go and tell your masters that the head of the Partistagno takes orders from nobody, and as they have invited me, so I invite them to come and find me in my castle of Caporetto above Gorizia, where they will get a triple dose of what you have got.'

With these words he led him tottering to the castle threshold where he gave him a push that sent him headlong out about ten paces, amid the guffaws of the bystanders. And then, while Messer Grande, still feeling his bones and gently touching his nose, went towards Udine in a hand-barrow requisitioned along the road, the Partistagno and his buli made all speed for Caporetto, whence he was not again seen on the lands of the Most Serene Republic. Old persons say that of his two companions lodged in the dungeons no word was ever heard again.

These trifling incidents took place in the Friuli about a hundred years ago and seem like stories dug out of Sacchetti. Such was the temper of the mountain lands, that for long the memory of ancient times was preserved among their granite peaks; but since the Friuli is a little compendium of the universe, mountainous, level and marshy by turns within its sixty miles from east to west, so one found there also the other side

of the medal. In fact at the Castle of Fratta during my childhood they always spoke of the castellans of 'up there' with
horror, so deeply had venetianism entered the blood of those
good Counts. And I am sure that they were even more scandalized than the inquisitors themselves at the entertainment
afforded to Messer Grande by the Partistagno.

But the justice, high, low, public, private, legislative and
executive, of the Fatherland of Friuli has driven from my
mind the great hearth, around which in the light of two tiny
lamps and the flickering flames of the juniper, I was recalling
the figures who used to sit there in the long winter afternoons
in the days of my childhood: the Count with his shadow, Monsignor Orlando, Captain Sandracca, Marchetto the serjeant and
Ser Antonio, the leading figure of the commune of Fratta. I
have not yet spoken of this last personage and it would need a
long disquisition to give any idea of what was the precise standing of this half-countryman, half-gentleman, midway between
the signori and the peasants. What he was in truth would be
too intricate to try and understand, but what he tried to appear
to be I could say in a few strokes of the pen. He wanted to
appear the most humble servant of the castle and the confidant
of the castellan and therefore the second patron of the countryside. Those who had good character turned this singular ambition to the good, but those on the other hand who were by
nature sordid swindlers became in this office the lowest and
most evil of the whole gang. Ser Antonio was among the
former; although he was prudent and talkative, he was at
heart one of the best fellows in the world and would not have
pulled the wings off a wasp even after being stung. The servants, the grooms, the town-crier, the scullions and the cook
were bread and cheese with him and when he was not taken up
with the Count, he used to joke with them and help the bailiff's
small son to pluck little birds for the spit. But as soon as the
Count chanced to appear, he pulled himself together and paid
attention only to him, as if it were sacrilege to attend to anything else when one had the good fortune of basking in the
effulgence of a magistrate. And according to His Excellency's

probable desires, he was the first to laugh, to say yes, to say no, and even indeed to contradict himself rapidly when his first thrust had gone awry.

There was also a certain Martino, a former valet to the father of His Excellency, who was always pottering about the kitchen like an old hunting dog long retired, and wanting to poke his nose into cupboards and casseroles to the great desperation of the cook, always grumbling about the cats which got between his legs. But being deaf and not much inclined to chatter, he did not join in the conversation. His one task was to grate the cheese. It is true that with his naturally phlegmatic nature made more so by age, and with the extraordinary quantity of minestra consumed in the kitchen, this task kept him occupied for many hours a day. I can still hear the monotonous sound of the rinds being drawn up and down the grater with the minimum respect for his nails, and in proof of his parsimony old Martino always had the tips of his fingers torn and plastered with cobwebs.

But it is not for me to make fun of him. He was, if I may say so, my first friend and if I wasted a good deal of breath trying to penetrate his eardrums with my words, I had for him through all the years that we lived together a tender affection. It was he who would come to look for me, when some impertinence committed had put me in Coventry with the family; he would make excuses for me to Monsignor when, instead of serving him, I had escaped into the vegetable garden to look for birds' nests; he bore witness to my illnesses when the Rector was hunting for me to give me my lesson in catechism and if they sent me off to bed, he was even capable of swallowing the oil and jalap in my stead. In fact, Martino and I were as hand and glove, and if on entering the kitchen I was unable to see him in the deep shadows that reigned there during the day-time, some inner sentiment would warn me if he were there and lead me directly to him, to pull his wig or ride horseback on his knees. If Martino was not there, everyone would ridicule me because I remained so quiet and timid like a chicken far from the hen; and in the end I would take to my heels, unless a rasp of the

36

Signor Count held me rooted to the floor. Then I would stand so deathly still that not even the Epiphany witch could have made me move, and only after he had gone out did I recover freedom of thought and movement. I never knew the reason of this strange effect produced on me by the tall and rigid old man; but I believe that his scarlet trappings used to hypnotize me like a chicken.

Another of my great friendships was with the Serjeant who sometimes placed me on the crupper behind him on his pleasure trips for the sticking of eviction notices and similar duties. But I did not have a hatred for knives and pistols like Captain Sandracca and on the way used to forage in Marchetto's pockets to try and steal his dagger and make a thousand childish defiances at the peasants whom we met.

On one of these jaunts to Ramuscello to carry a summons to the local castellan, the Serjeant had taken his pistols with him. I was rummaging in his pockets despite the slap he had given me a while earlier, and pulled the trigger, so that I injured one of my fingers: it is still a little curved and maimed in the top joint in memory of my praetorial excursions. This punishment, however, in no way cured me of my passion for arms, and Marchetto asserted that I should turn out to be a good soldier, and said that it was a pity I had not been brought up in one of the districts 'up there' where young people were taught to be accustomed to arms and not to chase peasants or play cards with priests and old women.

Martino, on the other hand, was not at all pleased at my escapades. The country people, though not turbulent and quarrelsome like those of Piedemonte, were likely enough to revolt now and again at the sentences of the Chancellor and to look askance at the Serjeant who enforced them. And with Marchetto's hot blood, who knew what might happen? Marchetto, however, claimed that my presence made him restrain himself and prevented him from doing anything rash; for my part, I used to boast that in an emergency I would have given him a hand reloading his pistols or striking desperate blows with my pruning-knife and, morsel that I was, felt offended

37

that others should laugh at these vaunts. Martino bent his head, understanding little enough of our talk, but went on muttering that it was not prudent to expose a boy to the reprisals that might be taken against a serjeant going to levy charges or affix notices of taxes and confiscations. In truth, those very peasants who cut so poor a figure in the Cernide and trembled in the Chancellery at an official glance, knew well enough how to handle a gun or an axe in their own houses or in the countryside.

As for me, though at first I used to marvel at these inconsistencies, I now feel that I have found the true reason. We Italians have always a natural antipathy for jacks in office, and we laugh at those who set themselves up above us, to whom we should raise our hats. Now this troop of men, herded together like sheep, marshalled into ranks to the sound of a kettledrum and animated with squeaks of the fife, whose valour was regulated by some curt word from their commander, always seemed to them a famous company of marionettes; the more so since their appearance was almost always unfavourable and only very rarely to advantage. Thus the idea of entering such a troop and looking like a doll, so disgusted them that every wish to do well and every feeling of dignity entirely disappeared.

I am speaking, be it understood, of times past; now the consciousness of a great aim may have improved them in this respect. But even now, philosophically speaking, it would not perhaps be wrong to think as one thought at that time; and the wrong lies in the fact that it is always rash to be wise and act according to the tenets of wisdom when all others are mad and behave according to their madness. It has been said and said again a hundred times, and proved up to the hilt, that one of us can stand firm and make any of the bravest of other nations turn tail. But on the other hand there is certainly no nation where it is more difficult to recruit an army and make it sound and disciplined as the military art to-day demands. Napoleon, indeed, showed the world, once and for all, that we have no lack of military valour, but only the desire and the

38

constancy of leaders. Furthermore, our perverseness in refusing to abdicate our freedom of choice, and our independent and rational temperament, is perhaps excused by our complete lack of military traditions. But enough of that as regards the people of Fratta; and as for their tremors in face of authority, it is not out of place to add that it was not so much the result of cowardice as of centuries-old reverence, and the fear always shown by illiterate persons for those who know more than they. A Chancellor who with a few strokes of the pen can at his caprice expel two, three or twenty families from their houses in misery and hunger must have seemed to these poor devils little less than a wizard. To-day, when public affairs move more surely, even the ignorant look upon justice with a more favourable eye and are not frightened at it as if it were the sister of the gallows.

In company with the various persons whom I have so far mentioned, the Rector of Teglio, my master in catechism and calligraphy, used to pass long hours in the inglenook of the great hearth, facing the Signor Count and making him deep bows whenever he was vouchsafed a word. He was a good priest from the mountains, and incidentally no friend of the town clergy, and so pitted with the smallpox that his cheeks always put me in mind of a stracchino cheese, when, as the gourmands say, it is very fat and full of eyes. He walked very slowly, spoke even more slowly, never omitting to divide every sentence into three parts; and this habit had become so much a part of his being that when eating, coughing or sighing it always seemed that he divided his eating, coughing or sighing into three parts also. All his movements were so ponderous that if he ever had happened to commit some sin, despite his usually quiet and evangelical life, I doubt if the Good Lord could have been induced to pardon him for it. Even his glances were not given without some weighty motive and seemed only with difficulty to penetrate the two hedges of eyebrows that protected them. He was the very ideal of premeditation, descended to become incarnate in the body of a mountaineer from Clausedo; tonsured by the Bishop of Porto, he wore the

39

longest hair doublet that had ever competed with a priest's calves. His hands used to tremble a little, which somewhat hindered him in his role of a calligrapher, but it did not prevent his leaning firmly on his malacca cane with a real horn handle. Concerning his moral qualities, even though he was born in the eighteenth century, he was a model of ecclesiastical independence. The exceedingly deep bows that he made to the Count did not prevent his carrying on his cure of souls in his own manner, and were perhaps equivalent to saying: 'Most Illustrious Signor Count, I venerate and respect you; but in my own house, it is I who am master.'

The Chaplain of Fratta, on the other hand, was a scared and pusillanimous little grasshopper who would have given the benediction with a kitchen ladle had the Count had the whim to ask him to do so. Not for lack of religion, but because the poor devil became so flustered when faced with the gentry that he really did not know what he was doing. Whenever he had to stay in the castle, he seemed to be on thorns; and I believe that, now he is dead, had God desired to give him a real Purgatory, he could have imagined nothing better than to allow him another life in the person of a house-steward. There was no one more able than he to remain seated for hours and hours without ever lifting his eyes or moving a finger when others were watching; but he possessed an equally miraculous art of disappearing without being seen, even from a company of ten persons. Only when he followed the Rector of Teglio did some flash of clerical dignity illuminate his countenance, but it was clearly to be seen that on such occasions it was an effort for him to keep behind his superior and he was so occupied in bearing in mind the part he had to play that he neither heard nor saw anything and was capable of putting live coals instead of hazelnuts into his mouth, as the factor had once tried this experiment on him for a bet. Signor Ambrogio Traversini, factor and valuer for the castle, was the poor chaplain's cross. Between those two there were always jokes and larks so in fashion in past times and which, in country gatherings, took the place of reading the newspapers. The Chaplain, as if in

40

duty bound, was always the butt of these jests, and was rewarded by an occasional invitation to lunch, a reward more cruel than the misadventure itself. In the greater number of such cases, his obsession with these invitations gave him a double quartan fever so that he had no need of lies in order to excuse himself.

Once, however, he was able to set foot on the farther side of the drawbridge, no man, I believe, felt happier than he, and that was the recompense for his martyrdom. He leapt, he ran, he rubbed his hands, his nose, his knees, took snuff, whispered ejaculations, passed his stick from one arm to the other, talked, laughed and joked with everyone and caressed everyone he found to hand, were it a boy, an old woman, a dog or a young cow.

I first had the glory and the malice to reveal the strange jubilation of the Chaplain at every escape from the castle, and once I had made the discovery, everyone, as soon as he left, rushed to the windows of the dining-hall to enjoy the spectacle. The factor swore that, some time or another, he would have leapt into the fishpond for excess of consolation; but it must be said in praise of the poor priest that this accident never once happened.

The greatest sign of joy that he ever gave was once when he joined the local urchins behind the church in ringing the festival bells. But that day he had really had a lucky escape. There had come to the castle a prelate of Porto, known as the Canon of St. Andrea, a great theologian and little tolerant of others' ignorance, who had honoured in the past and continued to honour the Countess with his spiritual ministrations. With Monsignor Orlando and the Rector, he had taken his place on a bench near the hearth and begun to dogmatize about morals. The chaplain who had come to make his usual enquiry about the digestion of the Signor Count, as he did every afternoon, nearly fell into the snare; but half-way into the kitchen he had overheard the voice of the theologian and, protected by the shadows, had taken to his heels, thanking all the saints in the calendar. Judge for yourself, if he had not every right to ring the bells for joy!

41

Besides these two priests, and the other clergy from the city, who frequently came to visit Monsignor di Fratta, the castle was frequented by all the lesser gentry and castellans of the neighbourhood, a mixed bag of tipplers, idlers, rogues and agreeable fellows who wasted their time in hunting, in disputes, in flirtations and in endless suppers, and pandered to the aristocratic pretensions of the Signor Count. When they came it was a day of turmoil. The best casks were broached, and many flasks of Picolit and Refosco lost their necks; and the young assistants of the cook took refuge in the scullery. Then the cook knew neither friends nor enemies; she ran hither and thither, sticking her elbows into Martino's stomach, trampling on Monsignor's feet, plucking ducks and eviscerating capons. Her activity was only surpassed by the turnspit, who shouted and dripped oil on all the pulleys in his task of turning three or four spits, loaded with hares and game. The tables in the hall and in two or three adjacent rooms were put together, and the fire in the great gallery fireplace was lit, which was so large that to keep it filled needed a good half standard of wood. It was noticeable that after the first outburst of the flames, the company had to take refuge behind the most distant walls or in far corners to avoid being roasted.

The gentlemen used to make the most infernal uproar, but for the most part the witty sallies were confined to some petty doctor or another, some minor priest or some poet from Porto-gruaro, none of whom ever failed to rush to the odours of the feast. At the end of the long tables some sonnet used to be improvised, though the rough draft, with corrections, was doubtless at home. But if memory failed, the usual round of congratulations and excuses for the liberty never lacked and the company 'if it were permitted' hastened to drink wine and to praise the infinite merits of the Count and Countess.

The most frequent of such visitors was an elegant and pow-dered advocate who in his youth had paid court to many Venetian ladies and was then living on memories in the company of his housekeeper. Another youth called Giulio Del Ponte always arrived with him, prided himself on competing

42

with the most subtle verses and used to enjoy making him lose his senses by emptying his glass once too often. The comedy finished in the kitchen with great guffaws behind the doctor's back, but the young man, who had been at Padua, behaved so well that he remained in better grace than ever.

This one, and a pale, taciturn young man from Fossalta, Signor Lucilio Vianello, were the only ones of that semi-plebeian rabble to have remained in my memory. Amongst the gentry, I can still remember a Partistagno, perhaps a kinsman of he who had received Messer Grande, tall, bold and strong, and with a certain haughty reserve of manner which contrasted strikingly enough with the fuddled licence of the mob. And from then onwards I remember to have noticed certain hostile glances pass between him and Vianello which certainly did not denote any good feeling between them. In truth, it was just these two who should have been able to get on together, since all the rest were a common scum of rogues and nitwits.

When I began to think for myself and was already able to scare the hens in the courtyard of Fratta, the only son of the Count had already been a year in Venice with the Somaschi Fathers, where his father had been educated before him; therefore I remember nothing of him, save an occasional slap he had given me before leaving to prove that he was the master; and at that time I was still a baby hardly able to gnaw a crust. Old Martino had then undertaken my defence, and I can still recall a good ear-pulling given by him to the young master, who rushed away screaming to the rafters; and Martino got a good dressing down for it from the Count. Luckily for him he was deaf!

As for the Countess she only appeared in the kitchen twice a day, in her role as controller of household affairs; the first in the morning to distribute the flour, butter, meat and other needs of the day, the second after the last lunch session to control the division of the food sent down from the patronal table to the servants, and to rearrange the rest in smaller plates for supper.

D
43

She was a Navagero of Venice, a tall gruff noblewoman, curt of speech, who snuffed tobacco in one nostril after another and never moved without the tinkle of the key at her belt. She always wore on her head a white lace cap flecked with rose at the temples like that of a young bride; but I believe that she did not wear it from vanity but simply out of habit. A noose of tape hung round her neck with a black silk kerchief, whence dangled a little diamond cross which, to quote the cook, would have furnished a dowry for all the girls of the district. On her breast, set in a gold brooch, she wore the portrait of a handsome man in a flowing wig, which was certainly not that of her husband; since he had a huge and malproportioned nose, while the man in the portrait on the other hand had a most delicate little nose, a real toy for smelling rosewater or Naples essence. To put briefly what I came to know later, the noble lady had most half-heartedly been constrained to this marriage with a castellan of the terraferma, and it seemed to her that she had fallen into the hands of the barbarians, accustomed as she was to the refinements and pastimes of the Venetian damsels. But forced to make a virtue of necessity, she had done her best to remedy this misfortune by dragging her husband with her from time to time to Venice and had there made up for her provincial retirement with luxuries, gallantries and being courted by all the most famous dandies. The portrait that she wore on her breast might well have been of one of the boldest of these; it was said that he had died of a chill from the night air, caught while he was with her in a gondola, and after that she would not ever hear of Venice and had retired to Fratta, to the great complacency of the Signor Count. At the time this terrible affair happened, the lady was close to her forties. Otherwise, the Countess passed long hours at her prie-dieu and whenever she encountered me, either at the door of the kitchen or on the stairs, she would give a little tug to the hairs on the nape of my neck, the sole gentleness that I ever recall having received from her. A quarter of an hour a day she employed in assigning her duties to the chambermaid, and the balance of her time she passed in one of the small salons with her mother-in-law and

44

her daughters, knitting stockings and reading the life of the saint of the day.

The old mother of the Count, the former Lady Badoer, was still living at that time; but I only saw her four or five times, for she was relegated to the wheel-chair of age and I was forbidden to enter any room save the one in which I slept with the second chambermaid or, as they used to call her, the children's woman.

The old Countess Badoer was an old woman of almost ninety, still fairly plump and with an expression showing goodness and common sense. Her voice, sweet and quiet, despite her years, had such a charm for me that I often risked getting a few slaps to go and listen to it, with my ear at the keyhole of her door. Once, when the chambermaid suddenly opened the door when I was in this position, she noticed me and beckoned to me. I think that my heart was ready to leap out of my breast with relief when she put her hand on my head and asked me sternly, but without a trace of harshness, what I was doing there. I answered simply, yet trembling with emotion, that I was there because I liked to hear her talking and that her voice pleased me very much and seemed to me like what I should have wished my mother's to have been.

'Good, Carlino,' she replied. 'I will always talk to you with kindness so long as you deserve to be well treated for your good behaviour; but it is not good for anyone, and least of all for little boys, to listen behind doors. When you want to talk to me, you must come into the room and sit near me, and I will teach you, as well as I can, to pray to God to make you a good boy.'

When I heard those words, poor little wretch that I was, the tears came running down my cheeks. It was the first time that anyone had spoken to me from their heart; it was the first time that anyone had made me the gift of a kind word and a caress; and that gift was from an old woman who had seen Louis XIV! I say seen, really seen, for the husband of the noble Lady Badoer, that old Count so covetous of grand-masters and admirals, had gone a few months after his marriage to France

45

as Ambassador of the Most Serene Republic and had taken with him his wife, who for two years had been the jewel of the Court.

This same lady had then returned to Fratta where she had retained the same graces of manner and of speech, the same rectitude of conscience and the same spirit of moderation and charity, so that, although she had lost the flower of her beauty, she had continued to enchant the hearts of her vassals and the inhabitants of the castle as she had previously so enchanted the hearts of the courtiers of Versailles. So true is it that real dignity is admirable and admired everywhere and neither becomes, nor is considered, less whatever may be the changes of its dwelling.

I wept copiously, pressing and kissing the hands of this venerable woman and promising in my heart to make frequent use of the largesse granted me to go and talk with her, when the real Countess, she of the keys, entered and gave a little start of indignation on seeing me in the little salon against her express orders. This time the tug at the nape of my neck was longer than usual and accompanied by a solemn rebuke and an eternal prohibition ever to enter these rooms again unless called for. As I went down the stairs, scratching the back of my neck and weeping this time more from rage than from grief, I could still hear the voice of the old woman, which seemed to become even sweeter as she interceded in my favour, but a scream from the Countess and a violent banging of the door, which was locked behind me, prevented me hearing the end of the scene. So I went down, one foot slowly after the other, to find consolation with Martino in the kitchen.

This friendship of mine with Martino was also not to the liking of the Countess or the factor, who was her right-hand man; according to him my teacher ought to have been a certain Fulgenzio, half sacristan and half writer in the Chancellery, who enjoyed within the castle the reputation of a spy. For my part, I could not stand this Fulgenzio and played him several tricks which must have made me insupportable to him also.

Once for example, though this happened later, I was in the

46

choir behind him during matins on Holy Wednesday, and seized the opportunity of his meditations to remove the taper from the cane with which he used to light the candles, and which was already lit, and to attach it to his coat-tail. When the taper was almost consumed, the fire caught his coat-tail and thence extended to the tow of his wig, and Fulgenzio began leaping about the choir and the boys who held the lutes began running round him shouting: water, water! In this commotion the luteboys rushed around and created such an uproar that the ceremony had to be postponed for a good half-hour. Nobody knew exactly what had been the cause of the scandal and I, who was suspected of being its author, had sense enough to play the Indian: but for all that I earned the fee of a day in my room on bread and water, which certainly did not put Fulgenzio any the more in my good graces, even as the conflagration in his wig had certainly not contributed to put me in his.

I have already said that the Countess spent the greater part of her spare time knitting stockings in the little salon in the company of her daughters. The last of these, in the years I am now recalling, was still quite a baby, younger than I by some years, and who slept in my room with the 'children's woman', who was called Faustina.

The Pisana was a lively baby, restless and petulant, with lovely brown eyes and very long hair, who already at three years old knew all the arts of a little woman and would have justified those who hold that women are never children, but are born full blown with all the elements of their attractions and their malice. There was not an evening before I went to bed that I did not bend over the cradle of the little girl and look long at her; she lay there with her big eyes closed, one tiny arm out of the bedclothes and the other curved over her forehead like a little angel asleep. But while I was enjoying her beauty, she would suddenly open her eyes and, overjoyed to have taken me in with her pretence of sleep, jump up in bed, giving me great slaps. This used to happen when Faustina was looking the other way, or when she had forgotten the instructions given her, for the Countess had told her to keep me at a

47

respectful distance from her little angel and not allow me to get too intimate with her. For me, there were the sons of Fulgenzio, who seemed to me even more abominable than their father, and I never let pass an opportunity of making trouble for them, especially when they went piping to their father that they had seen me give a kiss to the little Countess, or had carried her in my arms from the sheep-pond to the edge of the fishpond. But the little girl paid as little attention as I to others' remarks and continued to love me and try to make every possible use of me in her childish affairs, rather than of Faustina or Rosa, the other chambermaid, or 'the woman with the keys', whom we should to-day call the wardrobe-mistress.

I was happy and proud to have at last found a creature who believed me to be of use, and took a certain air of importance when I told Martino: 'Give me a good piece of string to take to the Pisana.' It was so I called her to him, though with all the others I dared not call her anything but 'the little Countess'. But these joys were not without their torments, since, alas, it is as true in childhood as in all other ages that there is no rose without thorns. Whenever the gentry of the neighbourhood arrived at the castle, with their well dressed and tidy children, with their starched collars and plumed hats, the Pisana left me at once to coquet with them and my nose was quite put out of joint in watching her make dainty little steps, twisting her neck like a swan and enchanting them with her sweet and ingenuous chatter. I would run to Faustina's mirror to make myself beautiful too; but, alas, I very quickly saw that I could not succeed. My skin was dark and smoked like a herring, my shoulders were badly set, my nose covered with spots and scratches and my untrimmed tangled hair stuck out around my head like the bristles on a hedgehog, while my trousers were torn and rumpled like the tail of a blackbird escaped from the limed twigs. It was to no purpose that I martyred my scalp with combs, sticking out my tongue with the intense effort I put into it; that unruly hair was even more tangled than ever. Once I had the idea of putting oil on it as I had seen Faustina do; but fate ordained that I should mistake the phial and

48

instead of oil I poured on my head a little bottle of ammoniac that she kept in case of convulsions and which gave me for a whole week the aroma of a compost-heap strong enough to turn one's stomach. In short, I was most unlucky in my first vanities and even while I tried to make myself more agreeable to the little one and wean her away from her new guests, I afforded her and them fresh material for laughter and myself yet another reason for fury and degradation.

It is true that once the strangers had departed, the Pisana returned to amuse herself by playing the mistress over me, but the ill humour of such infidelities was slow to dissipate and, without knowing how to liberate myself, I began to find her caprices too various and her tyranny a little hard. But she, the little devil, paid no heed. Perhaps she had guessed the stuff of which I was made and redoubled her oppressions, and I, for my part, my submission and affection, since in some natures devotion to those who torment them is even greater than gratitude to those who make them happy. I do not know if such beings are good or bad, wise or stupid; I only know that I was an example of them and that my fate has been such for all these long years of life. My conscience is not ill at ease either with the means or the results; and that contented, all is contented, at least in my own case.

I must however confess, in honour of the truth, that however talkative, flirtatious and cruel the Pisana showed herself even from the tenderest age, she never lacked a certain generosity, the generosity of a Queen who, after having buffeted and reviled some too ardent suitor, would intercede in his favour to the King, her husband. Sometimes she would kiss me repeatedly like a lapdog and enter into the most intimate confidence with me, but a little later she would make me act as her horse and strike me with a switch with little regard for my neck or my cheeks; but when Rosa or the factor appeared on the scene to interrupt our games together, which were, as I have said, contrary to the Countess' instructions, she would shriek and stamp her feet and shout that she loved me more than all the rest and that she wanted to stay with me and so on

and so on, until, struggling and screaming in the arms of whoever took her away, her shouts passed into silence before the
dressing-table of her mother. These frenzies, I confess, were the
sole reward of my abnegation and later I thought many times
that they were more due to her pride and obstinacy than to any
love for me. But we should not mix the bold judgements of a
more mature age with the purest illusions of childhood. I did
not feel the blows which I often got for my arrogance in wanting to join the Contessina's games and went back, happy and
content, to the kitchen to watch Martino grate the cheese.

The other daughter of the Countess, named Clara, was
already a young woman when I first opened my eyes to the
things of this world. She was their first born, a tall, blonde girl,
pale and melancholy, like the heroine of a ballad or the
Ophelia of Shakespeare; though she had never read a ballad
and certainly did not know *Hamlet*, even by name. It seemed
that long association with her aged grandmother had reflected
in her face the calm splendour of that serene and venerable old
woman. Certainly there was no daughter who ever watched
over a mother with greater care than she in divining every wish
of her grandmother; and she always divined them, since the
continual company between them had accustomed her to understand them at a single glance. The Countess Clara was beautiful
as a seraph would be who passed among men without even
grazing the filth of this earth and without understanding its
impurity and grossness. But to the eyes of many she might
have appeared cold and this coldness could change into an
aristocratic hauteur. However, there was never soul more
modest and candid than hers, so that the servants quoted her
as a model of sweetness and goodness; and everyone knows that
when it is a question of the master's praises the vote of two
servants is equivalent in itself to a whole volume of sworn
testimonies. When her grandmother wanted a coffee or a
chocolate and there was no one in the room, she would not ring
the bell, but herself descended to the kitchen to give the order
to the cook; and while the cook was getting everything ready,
she would stand patiently leaning on the step before the hearth

50

and even give a hand in taking the pan off the fire. When I saw her standing like that the kitchen seemed to be bathed in a heavenly light and no longer that sad and darksome place of every day.

People may ask me why, in my descriptions, I always return to the kitchen and why in it, and not in the dining-hall or on the staircase, I have introduced my personages. But the reply is very easy and very natural! The kitchen was the habitual residence of my friend Martino and the one place in which I could stay without being scolded (perhaps because of the darkness which prevented my attracting general attention); it was the commonest recollection of my infancy; so that even as the townsman recalls with pleasure the public ways in which he played his first games, I for my part have my first memories interwoven with the smoke and the darkness of the kitchen at Fratta. It was there that I first saw and knew men; it was there that I experienced and reflected upon my first loves, my first sorrows, my first judgements.

So it happens that, as my life runs on like that of other men in many lands, in many rooms, in different dwellings, my dreams lead me almost always to a kitchen. It is, I know, an ambience of but little poetry, but I write to tell the truth and not to entertain people with poetical fantasies. The Pisana had so much horror of this dark abode, deep and badly paved, and of the cats that inhabited it, that she would seldom set foot there save to pursue me with strokes of a switch. But the Contessina Clara, on the other hand, showed no such disgust, and came there whenever she needed, without twisting her lips or pulling up her skirts as did, indeed, the more disdainful of the maids. Therefore I leapt with joy to see her there; and if she asked for a glass of water, I was happy to offer her one and to hear her say graciously: 'Thank you, Carlino!' Then I would go back to my den in a corner, thinking: 'Oh, how beautiful are those three words: Thank you, Carlino!'

A pity that the Pisana had never said them to me with so sweet and caressing a voice!

51

# II

THE principal effect produced upon readers of my first pages will certainly have been curiosity to know at last who was this Carlino. It was, indeed, a real miracle on my part, or if you will, a solemn fraud to lead you sauntering through a whole chapter of my life, speaking always about myself, without first saying who I was. But since I must, sooner or later, tell you, know then that I was born the son of a sister of the Countess of Fratta, and was therefore first cousin to the Contessina Clara and the Pisana. My mother had made, as I would call it, a runaway match wth the most illustrious Signor Todero Altoviti, gentleman of Torcello; she had fled with him on a galley going to the Levant, and they had been married at Corfu. But it seemed that the taste for travel had quickly passed, because four months later she had returned without her husband, bronzed by the suns of Smyrna and, in addition, quick with child. When she was delivered, I was at once sent without formality to Fratta in a hamper; and so I became a guest of my aunt on the eighth day after my birth. How welcome I was can easily be guessed from the manner in which I arrived. Meanwhile my mother, poor thing, was expelled from Venice at the demand of her family and had set up house in Parma with a Swiss captain. Thence she returned to Venice to ask forgiveness of my aunt and died in the Hospital without so much as a dog to mourn her fate.

These things were told me by Martino and his telling of them made me cry; but I had never discovered how he came to know them. As for my father, they said that he had died at Smyrna shortly after the flight of his wife, some said of a broken heart for this desertion, others because of desperation for his debts, yet others of a flux brought on by drinking too much Cyprus wine. But the real story was not yet known, and there was also current a vague rumour among the Levantine merchants that before dying he had become a Turk. Whether Turk or not, they had baptized me at Fratta, being in doubt whether this had been done in Venice, and since the task of finding me a name had been left to the Rector, he saddled me with the name of the saint of the day, who happened to be San Carlo. The good priest had no predilection for any of the Saints of Paradise and no desire to cudgel his brains to find any unusual name for me, and I am grateful to him, for experience has shown me that San Carlo was in no way less worthy than any of the others.

The Countess had only abandoned her brilliant life in Venice a few months before my hamper arrived; therefore you can understand that she looked on its contents with some little annoyance! With all the trials and tribulations that she had had, she had now to add to them a baby to put out to nurse—and furthermore the baby of a sister who had dishonoured both herself and her family and had so bungled her marriage with a semi-gaolbird of Torcello that even now no one had been able to get at the whole truth of the affair.

The Signora Countess therefore, from the first glance she cast at me, felt for me the most sincere hatred and it was not long before I was called on to feel the consequences. Firstly, it was considered unnecessary to bring a wet-nurse into the house for a little serpent issued from no one knew where. I was therefore consigned to the cares of Providence and circulated from house to house, wherever there were breasts to suck, like St. Antony's piglet or the Child of the Commune. I am milk-brother of all the children, all the calves and all the kids born at that time in the jurisdiction of Fratta and had, as nurse, in addition to all the mothers, the goats and the cows, all the old women and even men of the neighbourhood. Martino indeed told me how, seeing me sometimes doubled up with hunger, he had had to prepare for me a sort of paste of water, butter, sugar and flour with which he used to stuff me until the food reached my throat and stopped me from crying. And the same thing happened to me in many houses, when the breasts charged to feed me that day had already been drained dry by some hungry infant of eighteen months.

53

Having survived those early days by a real miracle, the porter of the castle, who was also the winder of the Tower clock and the armourer of the district, shared with Martino in the glory of seeing me make my first steps. He was a certain Mastro Germano, an old bulo of the past generation, with perhaps several murders on his soul, but who had certainly found a way to make his peace with the Lord God, since he used to sing from morning till eve as he collected droppings along the roads in a little cart in order to manure a tiny field that he had leased from the master. In the inn he drank his flasks of ribolla with a truly patriarchal serenity. To look at him, one would think he had the easiest conscience of the parish. And my recollections of him have led me to conclude that the conscience of each one of us is adjusted to his own degree, so that what for one may be merely sucking an egg is for another a most grave offence.

Mastro Germano in the days of his youth had killed quite a number of persons in the service of the castellan of Venciredo; but that account he thought was up to his master to clear with God and, as far as he was concerned, once his Easter confession had been made, he felt himself as pure as the water of the fountain. This was not a mere quibble to quiet his remorse, but a general maxim that had armed his soul with a triple cuirass against every melancholy. Once he had passed on to the payroll of the castellans of Fratta as chief of the cut-throats, he had taken to telling his beads, which was the chief occupation of his new subordinates, and had thus finally purged himself of the old leaven.

Now that he had passed his seventieth year, they had finally completed his satisfaction by granting him custody of the portal and superintendence of the clocks and he believed firmly that the way he had chosen was that which led surely to the Papacy. One may well believe that he and Martino were not always of the same opinion. The one was born to become the Black Cap of some Rialto patrician, the other educated in all the villainies and outrages of the Zaffi of that time; one had been with the diplomatic servant of a powdered magistrate, the other was the broken lance of the most intolerant of the lowland castellans. And whenever there was some dispute between them, I was always involved, each wanting to take me away from his adversary and boasting greater rights in my person. But for the most part they were in accord, with a tacit tolerance, and enjoyed in common the progress made by my little legs, and, one on each side of the castle drawbridge, they made me toddle from the arms of one to those of the other.

When the Countess, going out for her afternoon walk with the Rector of Teglio or some guest from Portogruaro, surprised them in these exercises of pedagogy, she would turn aside to give them a glance of excommunication, and if I stumbled against her she never failed to favour me with that tweak at the back of the neck, Then I, trembling with fright, took refuge in the arms of Martino, and the Countess went onward, grumbling at the childishness of 'those two old fools' as my mentors were known to the people of the kitchen. However that may be, I owe it to the efforts of 'those two old fools' that I became steady on my feet and even able to escape under the parish linden whenever I saw appear at the end of the avenue the white cap of my lady aunt. I call her aunt, now that the poor thing has been dead for a good half century, but then, as soon as I was able to pronounce a word, they taught me at her command to call her the Signora Contessa, and so it always remained, our kinship being forgotten by common accord.

It was at this time that, having grown a big boy, and since it displeased the Countess to see me on the bridge, that they decided to hand me over to Fulgenzio the sacristan, of whom you already know my opinion. The lady thus believed that she would keep me away from her Pisana, but that instinct of contradiction, which boys also have, against those who command them without good reason, made me remain even more attached to my exigent little lady.

It is true that, as we grew up, and found that we two alone were not enough for our games, we collected together all the

55

urchins of the neighbourhood, to the great scandal of the maids, who, for fear of their mistress, took the Pisana away as soon as they were aware of what was going on. This, however, did not worry us in the least; and since both Faustina and Rosa could think of little save their suitors, there was no lack of opportunity of their charge escaping them and returning to join us. As the band grew, there grew in her the ambition to hold court, and as she was a little girl, as I have said, rather too advanced for her years, it pleased her to play the little lady and there began childish love affairs, weddings, divorces, reconciliations; all childish games, be it understood, but which none the less showed the trend of her nature. But I do not want to imply that everything was as childish as one would believe, and I wonder how they allowed the Contessina to roll in the hay and play piggy-back with this one and that one, marrying in jest and making pretence of sleeping with her husband and displaying, in these delicate circumstances, the most realistic actions.

Who could have taught her such things? I could not say for certain, but I at least believe that she was born with an innate knowledge of such matters. What was still more remarkable was that she never stayed with the same lover or the same husband, but changed them with the moon. And the village boys, who shamefacedly and more out of respect and submission than anything else took part in such comedies, paid no attention at all. But I, with my fixed idea, felt a bitterness and an indescribable pang at the heart when I saw myself deserted and it was my turn to leave her alone with the little son of the bailiff or the son of the apothecary of Fossalta. For she was not very particular in her choice. It was enough for her to change, though it is true that she wearied more rapidly of the more dirty or unmannerly of them than of the others.

Now that I can think coolly of these things (they are matters of eighty years ago, or maybe a little less), I see that I ought to have felt proud, that I alone was sometimes able to boast of enjoying her favours for a full three days running and that

56

while the turn of the other little boys fell only once a month, mine came round almost every week. Weathercock as she was and arrogant in her dismissals, she was flattering and imperious in her demands. She had to be obeyed at all costs and loved as she desired; and she insisted too that we must laugh with her, for if she found her husband sulky she would get angry and strike him. I believe that no Court of Love was ever governed by any woman with so much tyranny.

If I dwell so long over these childish affairs it is because I have my own reasons and mainly because they do not seem to me so childish as they would to the common run of moralists. Leaving aside the fact that, as I have said a while back, even children have their own vices, this childish liberty does not seem to me in any way becoming or profitable, since the senses become stimulated before the sentiments, with great danger to the symmetry of a whole life. How many men and women of great judgement have inherited the shameful necessity of libertinism from the habits of childhood? Let us talk openly. The metaphor of likening man to a young and tender plant which bends or stands erect according to the skill of the cultivator has been often enough used for me also to use it as a comparison. But better than such a metaphor to explain my idea is the image of the cautery that, once open, can no longer be closed; the humours run together to this part and it is best to let them run or risk spoiling the whole organism. Given that the senses have awakened as far as they can in the years of ignorance, it may well happen that reason will be ashamed of them or will lament their sordid mastery; but whence will come the force to war against them and thrust them back to their role as subjects? Their development follows the trend given them in the beginning despite the dictates of reason and the blush that it may occasion; and so are formed those beings, half men or supermen as you will, wherein depravity is united to the height of intellect and, up to a point, the height of feeling. Sappho and Aspasia belong to the history, not the mythology, of the Greeks, and are two types of those souls capable of great passions but not of great affections, as so

57

many in our days, through the sensual licence that prevents children from being innocent even before they are capable of becoming guilty. It will be said that Christian education destroys the pernicious effects of these first habits. But setting aside that the time spent in destroying their effects, which could better have been employed in building up the character, is time lost, I believe that such religious education serves rather to conceal than to extirpate the evil. All know with what torments St. Augustine and St. Anthony tamed the desires of the flesh and conquered their temptations; but to-day few can pretend to be such saints as they, and how many will you find who practise equal abstinences to obtain equal results? It is a sign of the times that all are content to take things as they are, content to save the decencies with the cunning of the cat which, as says and counsels Ariosto, covers its own ordures.

I who have by nature a temperament rather far from tepid owe perhaps to this circumstance the fact that I emerged exempt from the disorders derived in our moral state from the precocity of the senses. As well as I can recall, the battles of the spirit awoke in me before those of the flesh and I learnt, by good fortune, to love before I learnt to desire. But the merit was not mine, as it was not the fault of the Pisana if her childish stubbornness, her arrogance and her unrecognized vices had developed her impetuous, variable and restless nature and her petulant, vehement and faithless instincts. From the sort of life that they let her lead as a baby and a young girl, there emerge heroines, but never prudent and temperate women; not good mothers, not chaste wives nor true and patient friends; there emerge creatures who to-day would sacrifice their lives for a cause for which the next day they would not give a button. It is, more or less, the school wherein are tempered momentary and very great virtues and also great and lasting vices, the school of ballerinas, of singers, of actresses and of adventuresses.

Ever since she was a little girl, the Pisana displayed a rare intelligence, but it was vitiated by the frivolities and vanities

58

to which she was abandoned. The wife of Captain Sandracca, Signora Veronica, who acted as her governess, had to exercise an exemplary patience to concentrate her little brain for a quarter of an hour on the task she had to complete. Certain of learning everything with the greatest of ease, the little girl would study the first part of her lesson and leave all the rest; but even so, as she fortified her facility of learning, so she generated that of forgetting. Praise would sometimes spur her on to show herself worthy, but a moment later some caprice would make her forget her brief ambition. Used to conduct herself solely according to the rules of her own temperament, she wanted to change amusements and occupations every moment, not knowing that this is the best method of becoming bored with everything and to find in life neither repose nor content and to end up by never feeling happy, for the very reason of wishing to be so in a hundred different ways.

The science of happiness is the art of moderation; but the little girl could not see this and gave way to her whims in this way because it was in her power to do so. Wanting always to command and to be the first in everything, it is not strange that she tried to set everything right with lies, when she did not know how to make others hold the very high opinion that she wished them to have of her. Since everybody flattered her and pretended to believe them, she accepted this good-humoured simplicity seriously and did not even try to make her fables credible. It often happened that to set one lie right she had to invent two more, and then four to justify those two, and so on indefinitely. But she was of a prodigious imagination and quickness. Without ever showing the least embarrassment or fear lest others should not believe, she paid no attention to the complications which might arise from her fancies. I believe they so much encouraged her that little by little she was not even able to discern herself the true from the false.

I, however, often had to hold the bag, but I held it with such awkwardness that the cat soon escaped, and she never showed the slightest scorn or regret; it seemed that she did not expect anything better of me, or perhaps considered herself so

E                          59

superior that her assertions ought never to be doubted for the contrary testimony of another. It is true that the punishments all fell on me, and that, from that viewpoint at least, her imperturbability was in no way meritorious. These punishments, moreover, touched me very frequently, for my daily games with her were a continual infraction of the orders of the Countess and without troubling who was to blame, the crime first to be punished was mine, since my back-sliding was the more obvious. In any case, no one would have dared to punish the Contessina except her mother, and she as a rule gave no more thought to her than she would to someone else's daughter. For the Pisana there was the 'children's woman', and up to the time when she was ten years old maternal vigilance was limited to paying two ducats a month to Faustina.

From ten years old to twenty the convent, and from twenty onwards Providence; that was the type of education that the Countess considered should free her of every obligation towards her female offspring. Clara, it is true, had left the convent while still very young to act as nurse to her grandmother; but her grandmother's room was in fact even stricter than a convent and the difference was only in name.

That dear Countess, abandoned by her youth and by the passions that had given her a hint of something that was not entirely selfish, was now so wrapped up in herself and in the care of her own health, temporal and eternal, that, save for her rosary and a good digestion, she found no other occupation that suited her. If she knitted stockings it was mainly from habit or because no one else had so light a hand to make woollens delicate enough for her fine skin. As regards the surveillance of the household, she kept a firm hand on it, because she guessed that by shutting her eyes she would have made her family too happy, and the joy of others did not please her, since she herself had had so little. Envy is the sin or the punishment of niggardly souls, and I fear that the nape of my neck owed its daily martyrdom to the rage of the Countess at knowing herself old while I was still a young boy. For that reason also she loathed Monsignor Orlando as much

60

as I did. The sight of a heart at peace and of those hands crossed over his paunch as if to hold in a superfluity of beatitude, gave her a twinge of anger, and she could not understand how it was possible to grow old so contentedly. But there was good reason for the difference! Monsignor Orlando had centred all his complacency in the contentment of his stomach, which is a passion that can be contented, perhaps even better, at an advanced age. While she on the contrary . . . but what will you? I do not want to say more, now that her skeleton will have been purified by fifty years of burial.

Meanwhile, we began to grow up and our temperaments to become better defined; caprices to become passions and the mind able to reason about them. Already the horizon of my desires had widened, for the kitchen, the courtyard, the hayloft, the bridge and the square no longer seemed to me greater than a universe. I wanted to see what there was beyond and, left to my own resources, every pace that I made outside my usual circle brought me the same joys as Columbus experienced in discovering America. I rose very early in the morning and while Faustina was still occupied with her household cares or in the rooms of the masters, I used to slip out with the Pisana into the vegetable garden or to the edge of the fishpond. These were our happiest hours, when the little chatterbox importuned me less and rewarded my servitude more amicably.

I have often noticed that the morning is more apt for peace of soul and that then even the most artificial natures find some breath of simplicity or rectitude. But as the day wears on, daily habits and considerations begin to assert themselves more and more, till towards evening or after nightfall we can observe the most grotesque affectations, the grossest lies and the most irresistible outbursts of passion. Perhaps it is also because the hours of the day are usually spent in the open air, where men feel less the slaves of their own passions and more obedient to the universal laws of nature, which are never the worst. I will not say, however, that the Pisana changed her behaviour or manner of speaking when she was alone with me. I understood very well that she was more appreciative of my

61

admiration than of my friendship or my confidence, and for that reason I never ceased to be for her pantomimes a sort of audience, however restricted and familiar. However, I must write what I now realize and not what I realized at the time. Then, I enjoyed these sweet interludes, believing that the Pisana who was so eager to please me was the real Pisana, and that the changes in manner that took place during the day were the effect of those around her.

At the hour of Mass (it was Monsignor Orlando who celebrated it in the castle chapel) the whole family, masters, servants, bailiffs, estate employees and guests, collected along the benches reserved for each class of persons. The Signor Count knelt alone at a prie-dieu in the choir facing the celebrant, and there acknowledged with much dignity the greetings of Monsignor as he went in and out, as well as the three swings of the censer as the Mass was sung. In the solemn benediction and in the Oremus the celebrant never omitted to bless by name, with a profound bow, the most excellent and most powerful Patron and magistrate, who then turned upon the whole assembly a haughty glance which seemed to indicate the exceeding height that divided him from the flock of his vassals. The Chancellor, the bailiff, the Captain, the gatekeeper and even the maids and the cook absorbed as much of that glance as was their due and then addressed similar glances at those who occupied places in the chapel inferior to them; the Captain would preen his moustaches and place his hand noisily on the hilt of his sword.

The ceremony over, all remained with bowed heads in meditation and turned towards the Altar of the Rosary if the ceremony had been at the High Altar, or vice versa, until the Signor Count rose, sighed deeply as he made the sign of the cross, replaced in his pocket his missal, his kerchief and his snuffbox, and moved gravely and stiffly towards the holy water stoup. Then, crossing himself again, he left the chapel after saluting the High Altar with a brief nod. After him came the Countess with her daughters, the kinsmen and guests, who bowed a little deeper, then the servants and estate employees,

62

who bent one knee, and lastly the peasants and country people, who bent both.

Now that the Lord seems to us very very far away, He seems also equally distant from all the social grades, even as the sun does not warm the summit of a campanile more than the base. But then, when He was held to reside a good deal nearer, greater or less distances were more easily discernible, and a feudal lord considered himself so much nearer than all the rest, that he might permit himself a greater degree of confidence.

Usually for half an hour before the daily Mass they looked for me to serve Monsignor, who intended thereby to grant me a sign of his especial favour over the sons of Fulgenzio. But I did not feel in any way grateful for this distinction and knew how to take my own precautions, so that more often than not whoever was sent to hunt for me returned with empty hands. As a rule I took refuge with Mastro Germano and did not emerge from his hole until the last bell had already sounded. In the meantime they would already have put the surplice on Noni or Manichetto, who with their wooden pattens always ran the risk of breaking their noses on the altar steps when changing positions during the Mass, and I only entered the church when I was sure that all danger was past. However, my tricks were quickly discovered, so that I received many rebukes from Monsignor before the kitchen hearth; but I always excused myself by saying that I did not know the Confiteor. And in fact, to justify this excuse of mine on the few occasions when I was trapped, I had always the prudence to halt and begin again as soon as I reached the *mea culpa*, and then repeated the manoeuvre two, three or four times, until Monsignor lost patience and finished it himself.

On these unlucky days, I had afterwards the pleasure of remaining shut up in a little room under the dove-cote with the missal, a glass of water and a greyish loaf until an hour before vespers. I used to amuse myself by dipping the book into the water and crumbling up the bread for the pigeons; and later, when Gregorio, Monsignor's valet, came to let me out, I ran at once to Martino, who was always certain to have kept some

63

lunch for me. During these hours I had the chagrin of hearing the voice of the Pisana playing with the other little boys without any apparent regret at my incarceration; and I then took such a dislike to the Confiteor that I rolled it into pellets and threw them down into the courtyard on those chatterboxes, together with whatever small stones and bits of mortar I could find in the corners, or scratch out of the walls with my nails. Sometimes I would shake the door with all my force and throw myself against it, battering at it with my elbows, feet and head until after half an hour of this uproar the bailiff never failed to come up and reward me with four strokes of his stirrup-leather. And this dose was repeated in the evening when they found that I had completely soaked and torn up my missal.

On ordinary days after Mass, everyone went about his own affairs until the hour for lunch; I, however, had plenty to do to defend myself against the Rector's manservant who came to look for me to take me to my lessons. Running here and there, I in front and he behind, I always ended by being caught, half dead with anger and fatigue, and then had to go with him at a trot for the mile between Fratta and Teglio to make up for lost time.

When I arrived at the Rectory, I would waste time each day in looking at certain pictures of Udine which adorned the walls of the entrance hall and then only with great difficulty were they able to shut me up in a small study where, after the first day's experience, everything was kept rigorously under lock and key for fear of my misdoings. I would amuse myself drawing on the walls faces of the Rector, with two bushy eyebrows, and a certain cap on his head which left the satiric intentions of the artist in no doubt. Often, during these artistic exercises, I would hear in the hall the stealthy step of Maria, the Rector's housekeeper, who came to the keyhole to see what I was doing. Then I would leap to the writing desk and with elbows well spread out and head low on the paper, rounded certain A's and certain O's, which took up half a page each and which, with the addition of another four or five clumsy letters, still more Arabic, ostensibly completed my daily

64

task. Or I used to shout B-a Ba, B-e Be, B-o Bo, with so demoniacal a voice that the poor woman fled, half deafened, to her kitchen.

At half past ten the Rector arrived, gave me some slaps for the unseemly scrawls that he saw on the walls, added others for my atrocious writing and then administered a third dose for the great lack of attention that I gave to his finger in reading my A. B. C. I remember that I often used to look away at some little red books in a bookcase near by and then, instead of applying myself to the next line, would always jump to the line V-a Va, V-e Ve, V-o Vo. . . . It was at this point that I would be interrupted by the third correction administered from behind, and I have never been able to realize the reason for the preference my memory demonstrated for the letter V, if not perhaps that it is one of the last ones of the alphabet.

My mistakes and my fidgeting and the doggerel that I wrote during my lessons have always remained in my mind as a sign of my bad behaviour and of the exemplary patience of the Rector. If ever I had to teach a little pig such as I was then to read, I am sure that by the first two lessons I would have pulled both its ears off, but I experienced no other inconvenience than to take them back home again somewhat lengthened. But this inconvenience, which continued and increased for four years, between the ages of six and ten, procured me the advantage of being able to read all printed letters, and to write sufficiently fluently so long as capitals were not in question.

The thrift that I have afterwards had all my life for full stops and commas I owe entirely to the continuous and liberal instruction of the excellent Rector. Even now, in proceeding with this story, I have had to refer for the punctuation to a friend, a writer to the Prefecture, or otherwise it would be from beginning to end one single long sentence and there would be no preacher alive whose voice would be capable of intoning it.

When I returned to Fratta and did not lose myself by the way in chasing 'bridegrooms' or salamanders, I would arrive just at the moment when the family sat down to table. The

65

dining-hall was divided from the kitchen by a long corridor which rose gradually for a couple of yards, so that it was sufficiently high to be able to tell from the windows in the hours of sunlight that it was still day. It was a vast square room, a good half of it occupied by a table covered with a green cloth and as big as two billiard tables. Between two embrasures looking on to the moat there was a huge chimney-place; opposite, between two windows giving on to the courtyard, was a walnut dresser and in the four corners were four smaller tables with candlesticks prepared for the evening's games. The rough chairs certainly weighed fifty pounds apiece and were all the same, very wide in the seat, bolt upright from feet to headrest and covered with black morocco leather, stuffed with nails, or so at least one might have judged from their softness.

The table was usually laid for twelve covers, four each on the two long sides, three on the side next to the corridor for the bailiff, the surveyor and the Chaplain, and a side free for the Signor Count. His lady consort, with the Contessina Clara, sat on his right, the Monsignor and the Chancellor on his left; the places between these and the other sides of the table were occupied by the Captain, his wife and the guests. If there were no guests, their places remained unoccupied and if they exceeded two, the Captain and his wife sought refuge in the spaces between the bailiff, the surveyor and the Chaplain. The latter, however, as I have said, almost always wriggled out of the honours of the patronal table, so that his plate, more often than not, returned clean to the kitchen. Agostino, the butler, served the places near to the Signor Count, and he from his high chair (he alone had a sort of throne that almost lifted his knees to the level of the table) gave him the sign to carve. When he had finished, the Signor Count chose the best tit-bits and then with a gesture motioned the platter to his wife, but while he was doing this with his right hand, his left was already occupied with eating.

The coachman and Gregorio helped in the service, but they were of very little assistance, because they were too occupied in pouring out for Monsignor, unlacing his napkin or giving

66

him great slaps on the back when a mouthful threatened to go down the wrong way. The Pisana, naturally, did not dine at the high table, which was an honour reserved for girls only after their years in a convent. She ate in a pantry between the dining-hall and the kitchen, with the maids. As for me, I gnawed the bones in the kitchen with the dogs, the cats and Martino. No one had ever dreamed of telling me where was my place or which my cover, so that my place was wherever I could find one, and instead of knife and fork, I used my fingers. But I deceive myself. To eat my soup, the cook had given me a certain ladle, which had the advantage of widening my mouth by a good two fingers. But they tell me that because of this my smile had assumed a pleasanter expression, and since I have always had white and healthy teeth, I do not want to complain. Thus Martino and I did not come into account either among the gentry who dined in the hall or among the servants, to whom the Countess after the meal gave their portions, so that we were left the privilege of scraping the plates, the frying-pans and the saucepans; and from those made up our meal. There was also in the kitchen a basket full of polenta hung on a hook; and when the scraps were not enough to satisfy me, it was enough for me to point to the polenta. Martino understood me; he would roast me a slice and then good-bye all my miseries!

The Serjeant and the sacristan, who had wives and children, did not as a rule eat at the high table; so too Mastro Germano, who cooked for himself and concocted certain mixtures of his own that I have never been able to understand how human palate could support. It was by no means rare that he would catch one of the multitudinous cats who populated the Count's kitchen and make of it a ragout and a roast to last him for a week. Therefore, although he often invited me to lunch, I always took good care not to accept. He held that the cat has a most exquisite flesh and that it is the best remedy against many diseases; but he never said these things in the presence of Martino and therefore I fear that he wanted to impose on me.

After lunch and before the Countess appeared in the kitchen, I used to rush out to meet the crowd of urchins who gathered at that time in the forecourt of the castle; and many of them followed me into the courtyard, where the Pisana joined us a little later to indulge in those prodigies of coquetry of which I told you a while back. You will certainly ask why it was that I myself went to call my rivals, who were later to give me so much annoyance. But the Contessina was so barefaced that she was quite capable of calling them herself if I did not do so; and this led me to pretend to do of my own accord what, with a double shame, I should be forced in any case to endure.

The tranquil digestion of the Countess and the affairs that occupied the women all afternoon left us free for our games; and if perchance the old grandmother asked in those hours to see her little granddaughter, the Pisana behaved so badly in her room that the Countess ended by sending her away as a dangerous disturber of her digestive processes. We had, therefore, full liberty to run, to shout, to pull one another's hair, in the vegetable garden and in the precincts of the castle. Only one terrace, overlooked by the windows of the Count Monsignor, was forbidden us by the incorruptible vigilance of Gregorio. Once when some of the boldest tried to evade this prohibition, the valet had emerged from the little doorway of a secondary staircase with a broom-handle and had so belaboured those disturbers of the peace that we all understood that there could be no joking with that question. The Count used to say that he occupied himself during those hours with the affairs of the Chancellery, but if this were the case, he must have enjoyed a most extraordinary sense of sight, since his windows always remained firmly shuttered until six.

As far as Monsignor was concerned, he slept and he said that he slept, but even had he wished to deny it, he snored so loudly that no one in any of the infinite corners of the castle would have believed him. Between six and half past, when the weather permitted, the Countess went out for a walk; and the Count and Monsignor usually went out to meet her half an hour later. They had no fear of not meeting her because she invariably walked at the same pace every evening as far as the first house of Fossalta and then turned back at the same pace, occupying

68

in the whole walk exactly seventy-five minutes, save for unforeseen incidents.

It is hardly necessary for me to say that the Chancellor went out with the Count; he used to walk a pace behind his master, amusing himself by kicking the pebbles on the pathway into the ditch when he was not honoured by any questions. But more often the Count would ask him about the morning's doings and he regaled him with accounts of the examinations that he had made and of the legal cases, the reports of which he spread out before His Excellency. These reports were, in fact, so many sentences to which His Excellency deigned to append his signature, putting on for that purpose a double pair of spectacles and using all the sweat of his calligraphic knowledge. While the two magistrates were discussing the affairs of this world, Monsignor Orlando would saunter on, passing his tongue over his teeth and caressing his paunch. The two companies met at the stepping stones on the old road at the border of the two districts. The Chancellor halted with his hat lowered to the ground, Monsignor made way with a wave of his hand, and the Count advanced half-way across the stepping stones to give his hand to the Countess. After them passed the Contessina Clara, though she often used to remain at home to look after her grandmother, and finally the Rector, the Chaplain, Signor Andreini or Rosa or whoever else of the band happened to be with them. They returned thus in company to the castle, walking two by two, or more frequently in single file because of the atrocious state of the road.

As soon as they arrived, Agostino ran to light the lamp in the dining-hall, a great silver lamp on which was blazoned, in place of the handle, the arms of the family: a wild boar between two trees with a Count's coronet above. The boar was larger than the trees and the coronet larger than both. Although the Count attached great value to this work, one could see at first glance that Benvenuto Cellini had had no hand in it. In the meantime, the cook put a great pan of coffee on the fire and the company waited in the dining-hall, continuing the conversation begun during the walk. But the afternoon was

69

only passed thus during the fine months and when the weather was dry. At other times, neither the Signor Count nor Monsignor ever left their rooms save to take a bench by the kitchen fire, and it was there that the family gathered until the hour for cards. At these times they would take their coffee at the hearth and then move together to the dining-hall, where the small tables had already been prepared and the whole company would follow them, walking on tip-toe. The Countess alone was there to welcome them, for the Contessina Clara did not come down until later, after she had seen her grandmother to bed.

Sometimes the Captain's wife had the good fortune to take coffee with the Countess and this was a sign that the affairs of the day could not have gone better. The Signora Veronica showed herself very haughty at this honour and looked her husband up and down when he stood before her, as was his usual custom, to preen his moustaches before sitting down. When the gathering was made up only of the family, two small tables of 'three-seven' were sufficient; but if there were visitors or guests, a thing that never failed to happen every autumn evening and on every Sunday during the rest of the year, the high table was invaded with 'merchant at the fair', or with a tombola. The puritans like Monsignor and the Chancellor, who did not like games of chance, retired into a corner to play 'three-seven', while the Captain, who declared that luck was always against him, went into the kitchen to play 'goose' with the Serjeant or Fulgenzio. The truth of the matter was, I believe, that the stake of three soldi, which was customary in the dining-hall, was too risky for him and he felt more at ease with the halfpennies or farthings of the kitchen.

I, however, after having played with the Pisana until sunset, when Faustina took her away to put her to bed, found myself a corner in the inglenook and made Martino or Marchetto tell me stories. So the evening passed until my head began to droop on my breast, when Martino took my arm and crossed the courtyard, so as not to pass through the dining-hall, and up the stairs to Faustina's door. There I would enter, groping and

70

rubbing my eyes, and having unbuttoned my trousers was already fully undressed and ready for bed, with a single wriggle, for neither shoes, nor waistcoat, nor stockings, nor drawers, nor neckwear of any kind ever complicated my toilet until the age of ten; a jacket and a pair of trousers of peasant homespun that was woven in the castle for the servants, together with a piece of cord to hold up my trousers, comprised all my personal attire. I had also one or two shirts, which compensated with their superabundance of material for all their other defects, since it was Monsignor who handed his on to me when they were worn out, and no one ever took the trouble to make them fit me save by shortening a little the tail and sleeves. As for my head, one winter when it was freezing hard, Mastro Germano had provided me with a huge fur cap which he had worn from the time when he was a bulo at Ramuscello. This cap would easily have slipped down to my chin if the Rector had not previously prepared my ears to prevent it ceding to the force of gravity, and Martino used to say that when I had that thing on my head I looked to him like an angry cat. But he said it perhaps to annoy Germano and I am grateful to him and his big cap, thanks to which I was saved from many a chill. Certain it is that I still had it when I became a young man and even saved it to wear at festas because my head, being thus made so much larger, seemed to suit me wonderfully and to give me a terrifying appearance.

One day, when I was at the fair of Ravignano beyond the Tagliamento, and they were dancing on the platform in the square, I took it into my head to make fun of some Cernide of the Savorgnani who had come to maintain order in the fair, with their muskets in one hand and napkins in the other filled with eggs, butter and salami to make what they called a 'scabby omelette'.

These Cernide with their wooden sandals, their jackets of threadbare homespun and their faces that radiated grossness a mile off, made me die with laughing, therefore I and one or two other louts from Teglio and the neighbourhood began to make horns at them and ask them if they were clever enough to turn

71

their omelettes and if they intended to cook them with their wooden sandals. One of them retorted that we would do better to go and dance, so I jumped in front of him and said that I would begin with him. In fact I did so and taking him by his arms, just as he was, with his musket still on his shoulder, led him around in the strangest furlana that was ever seen. But since he had put his provisions on the ground, it chanced that in our gyrations we stepped on the eggs and thus made his omelette before it was due. Then these valorous soldiers, who had not moved an eyelid to see their comrade thus derided, suddenly became much concerned at the destruction of the eggs and wanted to attack me with their bayonets. But I, taking my pistols from my pockets and pushing my ballerino flat on the ground, began to scream that the first man to touch me would be killed. In a moment my companions gathered round to defend me, one with an unsheathed knife and another with pistols like my own. There was a moment of suspense, and then commenced an uproar in which, I don't know how, we all found ourselves one on top of the other without either firing our pistols or using any other weapons save our fists, and indeed the occasion was not worth it. Beaten on this side and trampled on that, those poor Cernide emerged much the worse for wear, and their eggs the same, till their Captain of a Hundred arrived with the rest of the band and leapt into the fray, forcing them with dire threats to end this fracas; if not, he said, he would give the order to fire without regard to friend or foe.

Witnesses were then summoned to find out the culprits, but they, as always, backed us up and blamed the Cernide, so that we were let go without further trouble. But just as I was withdrawing, bragging to my companions at this triumph, the Cernida who had danced the furlana with me shouted after me that I ought to take great care not to lose my fur cap and that he would use it as a trophy to put on the head of his ass on the second day of the fair. I replied with a rude gesture from the square that he and his ass would make a pretty pair but that he would never lay hands on my crest.

Here the Captain of the Hundred cut us short, and we went away to dance with the prettiest girls of the fair, while the Cernide lit their fires to make their omelettes with the few eggs that remained to them.

That evening I stayed on at the festa longer than I had intended on my arrival, to see what the rogue who had taunted me intended to do; and so also did some of my companions. Then, at an hour of night when it was blacker than hell itself, we moved off towards the Mendrisio ferry where, on the further side, the bailiff's cart was waiting for me.

The road was low and winding, through a countryside thick with trees and in some places so narrow that four persons could scarcely walk abreast, but since every one of us, due to the abundant draughts of ribolla we had taken, needed room enough for four, there was always a good chance of someone falling into the ditch. We were laughing together and singing as well as we could with the wine gurgling almost to our throats, when at a turn of the road I saw something like a dark figure that leapt quickly over the ditch and flung itself on me like a bomb. I jumped back when a voice said: 'So it's you!' and I felt a heavy blow on the back that sent me rolling in the puddles like a sack of salt pork. As I was raising myself on my elbows I saw the same figure leap back over the ditch and disappear into the darkness of the countryside. It was only then that I realized that I had lost my hat and crawled along the road looking for it; but it must have been either that one could see the road from the surrounding country more easily, or that the darkness was in my own eyes, for he who had jumped the ditch saw me bending over to look for it and from a distance called out to me to set my heart at ease, because he had taken my crest to beautify his ass on the following day.

On hearing the words, I recollected the Cernida and the spirit returned to my companions, since to their eyes this apparition had all the appearance of a devil. But once known for what it was, they all wanted to have revenge at all costs; but the ditch was wide and no one sure enough of his legs to

73

try and jump, which was a sign that we still possessed a glimmer of sense. So we went our way, promising to return the next day. Thus it was that we all finally decided to spend the night at Mendrisio, and the next day returned to the fair, examining all the Cernide and all the asses that we came across. When we came on one that had between its ears my fur cap glued to its forehead with pitch, we gave such a drubbing to its master that he had afterwards to be loaded on to his own ass and sent home; and my cap, since it could no longer be worn, was glued on to his face, saying we would leave it to him as a souvenir.

That was the end of Mastro Germano's present that had given me such good service for so many years; and from that incident was later born a complaint which kept me pretty busy, as I shall tell you in its proper place. Meanwhile, I beg you not to lose your good opinion of me if you find me for once in my life creating an uproar and associating with peasants and pot-house brawlers. I promise that you will see me, more suitably, as a man of importance and, in the meantime, I return to being once again a small boy, in order to tell my story in the proper order.

I have told you that I used to go to bed while they were still playing cards in the dining-hall; but the game did not go on for very long, for at half past eight exactly it was interrupted to chant the Rosary and at nine the company sat down to supper, and at ten the Signor Count gave Agostino a sign to light his lantern. The company then filed to the door that led to the great staircase, on the far side of the room to that which led to the kitchen. I say great staircase in a manner of speaking, for it was an ordinary staircase like all the others; on the first landing the Signor Count always used to stop in order to make his prognostications for the next day by feeling the wall. If it were moist, the Signor Count would say: 'To-morrow will be bad weather,' and the Chancellor behind him repeated: 'Bad weather,' while all the others added with solemn faces: 'Bad!' If on the other hand he found it dry, the Count exclaimed: 'We shall have a most beautiful day to-morrow,' and

74

the Chancellor also: 'A most beautiful day,' and the others, down to the lowest step: 'Most beautiful!' During this ceremony the procession halted on the staircase, to the great distress of the Countess, who was afraid of getting sciatica amongst all those draughts. Monsignor, indeed, had time to drop into his first sleep and it fell to Gregorio to hold him up and shake him, otherwise every evening he would have rolled down on Signora Veronica who was behind him.

As soon as the whole band had reached the hall, the function of saying good night began, after which they separated each in search of his room; and some of these were so far away that there was plenty of time to recite three Paters, three Ave Marias and three Glorias before reaching them. So at least Martino used to say, who had been assigned a tiny room on the second floor next to the tower and close to the room destined to house any friars who might come to the castle on a mission.

The Signor Count and his lady occupied the room that from time immemorial all the heads of the most noble family of Fratta had inhabited. It was a large, very high room with a terrace that in winter gave one cold shivers even to look at, and with a ceiling of cross beams painted with yellow and blue arabesques. Terrace, walls and ceiling were all covered with boars, trees and coronets, so that one could not glance around without meeting a boar's ear, the branch of a tree or the point of a coronet. The Signor Count and the Signora Contessa, in their immense wedding bed, were literally invested by a phantasmagoria of family coats of arms and crests, and this glorious spectacle imprinted on the imagination before dowsing the light could not but instil an aristocratic character even to the most dark and secret functions of their matrimony. Certainly if the flocks of Jacob brought forth speckled lambs because of the withies that they saw at the watering place, then the Signora Contessa could only have conceived children convinced and blessed by the illustrious excellence of their line. That later events did not always justify this hypothesis could have been the fault of the Signor Count rather than of his lady.

The Contessina Clara slept near her grandmother in an

apartment that opened into the hall opposite to her parents' room. She had a little room that resembled a nun's cell; and the only boar, which was engraved on the stucco of the fire-guard, she had, perhaps without noticing, covered with a pile of books. These were the remnants of a library allowed to rot in a basement through lack of interest of the castellans and the combined assaults of worms, mice and damp. The Contessina, who in the three years spent in the convent had taken refuge in reading from the tedium and the gossip of the nuns, had remembered this room lumbered with torn volumes and vellums and set herself to fish about for the little of value that remained. A few volumes of memoirs translated from the French, some stories by those old Italians who wrote without exaggeration of household affairs, Tasso, Ariosto, the *Pastor Fido* of Guarini and almost all the comedies of Goldoni, printed only a few years before; that was all her spoils amounted to. Add to these an office of the Madonna and a few devotional works and you have the library behind which, in Clara's room, the family boar was hidden.

After she had gone to her grandmother's bed on tip-toe to make sure that nothing disturbed the placidity of her dreams, holding her hand in front of the lantern to lessen the reflection from the walls, she would withdraw into her little cell to pore over some of these books. Often all the other inhabitants of the castle were already sleeping soundly while the light of her lamp was still shining from the cracks of her balcony; and when at last she took up either the *Gerusalemme Liberata* or the *Orlando Furioso* (the identical volumes that had not been able to decide the military vocation of Monsignor her uncle) the oil failed in her lamp before the will to read from the eyes of the young girl. She lost herself with Erminia in the shady groves or followed her in the quiet dwellings of the shepherds; she passed her time with Angelica or Medoro in writing love songs on the mossy walls of the grottoes and raved with the mad Orlando and wept with compassion for him. But above all her soul was filled with pity for the end of Brandimante when the fatal hour cut short upon his lips the name of his love and it

76

seemed that his soul passed onwards to finish and repeat it continuously in the happy eternity of love.

When she dropped off to sleep after such reading, she sometimes in dreams thought herself the widow Fiordiligi. A black veil fell from her forehead over her eyes as if to seal off from the vulgar gaze the sanctity of her inconsolable grief; a sweet, melancholy, eternal sorrow expanded in her heart like the distant echo of weeping harmonies and from the purest substance of that grief there emanated a spirit of hope that, too delicate and ethereal to wander on the earth, flew upwards to highest heaven. She did not know it, but the affections of that Fiordiligi of her dreams corresponded exactly to the sentiments of the Contessina Clara.

A soul impervious to the impressions of this world, she was preserved as God had made her, among the frivolities, scandals and vainglories that surrounded her. And the devout beliefs and gentle habits of her grandmother, purified by the serene meditations of old age, were renewed in her with all the spontaneity and perfume of her virginal years. In her early infancy she had always remained at Fratta, the faithful companion of the infirm old woman. She seemed the young chestnut shoot that rises from the old stump, instinct with exuberant life.

This solitary existence had preserved her from the vicious company of the maids and from the lessons that she might have learnt from the example of her mother. She lived in the castle simply, tranquilly and innocently, like the swallow that conceals its nest under the rafters of the granary. Her beauty increased with her years as if the air and the sun in which she steeped herself from morning till eve, with the robust carelessness of a country girl, had mingled within her to develop and illuminate her. But it was a good growth and a light modest and pleasant like that of the moon, not the garish and glittering flicker of the lamp. Her appearance seemed to spread about her a devout and almost celestial peace; one scarcely understood, seeing her, that beneath this gentle and harmonious exterior the fervour of devotion was mingled with the poetry of a pure imagination, hidden and active, and with

77

the utmost delicacy of sentiment. She was the fire of the South reflected on the pure and shining ice-fields of the North.

The simple peasant women of the surroundings called her 'the Saint', and remembered with veneration the day of her first communion when, as soon as she had received the mystic bread, she had fainted from delight, from fear and from humility; and they said indeed that God had called her in an ecstasy as worthy of a still closer marriage with him. Clara too recalled, with joy mixed with terror, that celestial day, always relishing in memory that sublime rapture of the soul invited to participate for the first time in the highest and sweetest mystery of her religion.

The Contessina Clara, as well as being a believer, was devout and fervent, since to her faith was not enough, and she wanted love also. Her reputation for sanctity was not due merely to the fervour and frequency of her religious practices, but even more to her continual and active deeds of the most holy virtue. Her manner did not reveal the humility of the kitchen maid or the housekeeper, but that of the Countess who accepts from God the inequalities of society and who feels before him no higher than the most abject of the human family. She had what they used to call the gift of second sight to sense the afflictions of others and that of simplicity to become by common consent their counsellor and consoler. To wealth she gave that value that it assumes from the needs of the poor, its real value, as it should be established in a sane economy, to become blessed of humanity. People used to say that money slipped through her fingers; and it was true, but she paid no attention to it, regarding it as a duty to be done, even as we do not notice the blood that circulates in our veins or the lungs with which we breathe. She was completely incapable of hate, even against the bad, since she did not despair of their repentance.

All created things were her friends and nature never had a daughter more grateful and loving. She went so far that she could not see mousetraps in the house and when walking in a meadow went out of her way not to tread down some flower or fresh tuft of green grass. Without poetic exaggeration, she

78

had so light a step that the flower would bend only for a moment under her heel and the grass was scarcely aware that it had been trodden. If she kept little birds in a cage, it was only to set them free again at the coming of spring, and sometimes she became so familiar with these charming songsters that it pained her to have to separate from them. But what was her own pain to Clara when the good of others was concerned? She would open the door of the cage with a smile made more beautiful by tears, and sometimes the little birds would come back to peck at her fingers before flying away, and even remained a day or two in the vicinity of the castle, visiting with confidence the window where they had lived as happy prisoners throughout the evil season. Clara used to recognize them and knew the degree of affectionate remembrance they preserved. She thought then that the things of this world are good and that men could not be bad, if goldfinches and tomtits showed themselves so grateful and loving.

Her grandmother smiled at her from her armchair, watching these tender and moving girlish fancies of her granddaughter. And she took good care not to laugh at her, for the good old woman knew from experience that these delicate virginal feelings were preparing for her later age an inexhaustible source of pure and modest joys that were neither frail nor grudging. In the three years that she had lived in the Salesian Convent of San Vito, the girl had been ridiculed enough for her fancies, but she had the goodness of heart not to be ashamed of them and the constancy not to deny them. So that, when she went out again to take up once more by her grandmother's bed her duties of nurse, she was still the same Clara, modest and willing, quick to laugh and quick to tears for whatever affliction was not her own. The Countess, having only recently transplanted herself from Venice to Fratta, had found her still a little uncouth and had thought to correct her by the usual ten years in a convent, but after three years she began to say that Clara, being by nature clever, must have had enough of it. The truth was that the care of her mother-in-law weighed too heavily on her and in order not to have to sacrifice the services of a waiting woman for a whole year, it seemed a double saving to bring her daughter home again.

On the other hand her extravagances in Venice had somewhat unbalanced the family budget and being then concerned with providing for the education of her son, she wanted to curtail her expenses for her daughters. There were already two of them, for the Countess was carrying the Pisana when she decided to remove Clara from the convent and never doubted for a moment that she would deliver a girl, for whom, indeed, she had already chosen a name in honour of her mother, who was a Pisani.

So it was while I was sucking breasts and swallowing pap in all the houses of Fratta; but when I was nine and the Pisana seven, and the young Count Rinaldo was finishing his course of rhetoric with the Reverend Fathers Somaschi, the Contessina had already grown up into the perfect comeliness of a young woman. I believe she was then roughly in her nineteenth year, though she did not seem so old because of the delicacy of her complexion which always preserved the glow of youth. Her mind had been enriched by good examples from the books that she had been reading and with the finest thoughts in the tranquil development of a compassionate and meditative nature; her feelings kept her busy with the help that she gave to the poor women of the countryside while losing nothing of her childish graces. She still loved flowers and birds, though she now thought less about them since she had more important cares, but her serenity remained the same, made even more charming by an almost celestial assurance.

When, after having helped her grandmother to undress, she entered the dining-hall and sat down close to the little table where her mother was playing cards, with her white embroidery in one hand and her needle in the other, her presence drew all eyes and sufficed to moderate for a while the voices and the comments of the players. The Countess, who had wit enough to see this, noticed the effect produced by her daughter and was even mildly jealous of it; despite her white lace cap and all the pride of the Navagero house stamped on her features, she had never been able to achieve as much. When the chatter, often coarse and slanderous, of the company moderated, the momentary respite displeased her and she was the first to stimulate the Captain or Signor Andreini to continue and say their piece. The Signor Count stared in astonishment to hear his wife taking pleasure in the castle gossip and Monsignor glanced sharply at his kinswoman, not understanding the reason for these fits of affability, which were really unusual and perhaps a little shamefaced.

I was still then very small, but none the less from the keyhole whence I was sometimes a spectator of the play, I understood very well the anger or the good humour of the Countess; I also understood Clara, for I still remember that when the Captain or Andreini replied somewhat crudely to the invitations of the most illustrious lady, a delicate blush coloured her cheeks. It seems to me that I can still see that angel of a girl redouble her attention to her embroidery and, in her confusion, get her fingers tangled in the threads. I am quite sure that that blush was more due to timidity than anything else and that the thoughts that crossed her mind at those moments were not of unmixed pride. But how could Monsignor have been expected to understand or even suspect that? I repeat; I was nine years old and he over sixty; he was a canon with a long cloak and scarlet stockings, I almost a foundling, shirtless and barefoot. Yet, despite the fact that he was called Orlando and I Carlino, I knew more of the world and of morality than he did. He was the simplest theologian of the whole Catholic Church; I would put my hand in the fire for that!

About that time, the visits to the Castle of Fratta, for the most part by the youths of Portogruaro and the neighbourhood, greatly increased. It was no longer the privilege of Sundays or the evenings of harvest time, but all the year round, even in the hardest and most snowy winters, some courageous visitor arrived on foot or on horseback, with arquebus on shoulder and lantern slung high. I do not know whether the Countess claimed the honour of attracting these visits, certainly she used to take much trouble in making herself lively and gracious. But despite

81

the attractions of her respectable and more than mature years, the eyes of these signorini used to wander here and there until they finally rested on the charming little face of Clara. Vianello of Fossalta, being the nearest, was also the most assiduous; but the Partistagno was not far behind him, though his Castle of Lugugnana was on the seashore at the edge of the pinewoods, seven good miles from Fratta. This distance perhaps gave him the right to come rather earlier, and it happened many times that he arrived just at the moment when Clara went out to meet her mother on her walks. He would then ask for the honour of accompanying her and Clara would agree courteously, although the harsh and bold manners of the young cavalier were not much to her taste.

When they had finished playing cards, the Countess never failed to invite the Partistagno to spend the night at Fratta, always lamenting the dangers, the darkness and the length of his journey, but he would decline the invitation with a brief 'thanks' and, shooting a glance at Clara which was seldom, and then only by chance, returned, he would go to the stables to saddle his strong Furlana racer. Wrapping himself well in his cloak and settling the shoulder strap of his musket with the indispensable lantern on it, he would leap into the saddle and go out over the drawbridge at a sharp trot, assuring himself with one hand that his pistols were still in the side pockets of his saddlebags. He would then pass away like a ghost along those dark roads with their deep ditches, but for the most part would stop to sleep at San Mauro, about two miles away, where for greater comfort he had arranged for himself four rooms in a farmer's house on one of his properties.

The people of the district had a most wholesome respect for the Partistagno, for his musket and for his pistols, as also for his fists, should he be unarmed; for these fists were so heavy that after a couple of blows from them in the stomach, there was no need of shot or bullets to send a man to his creator.

Vianello, however, came and went every evening on foot, with a small lantern attached to his stick stretched out in front

82

of him like the sacristan's collection bag during the intervals of the sermon. He appeared to be unarmed; though perhaps had you searched his pockets you would have found an excellent double-barrelled pistol, an arm not too common at that time. But, being the son of the Fossalta doctor, he had his share of the paternal invulnerability and nobody would have dared to molest him. Doctors at that time counted, in popular opinion, in the category of wizards and no one felt bold enough to provoke their revenge. There are plenty of vendettas, still unknown, at the present day; in the last century there were three times as many and you may judge for yourself how many were carefully planned! The common people were almost able to believe that a doctor could bring the plague to an entire province and I know one patriarchal family of that district where, before calling in the doctor, they would recite several orations to the Madonna to pray that his visit should be accompanied by good fortune.

Doctor Sperandio (a good name for a doctor and which in itself gave good counsel to his patients) had nothing in his appearance to give the lie to the reputation of witchcraft with which he and his colleagues were honoured. He used to wear a huge fleece and horsehair wig, as black as ink, which well protected his forehead, his ears and his neck against the wind, as well as an enormous three-cornered hat, equally black and as big as a thunder-cloud. To see him from a distance on his bony and exhausted nag, ash-coloured like a donkey, he seemed more like a grave-digger than a doctor. But when he dismounted and put on his spectacles by a sick-bed to look at a tongue, he seemed more like a lawyer preparing to draw up a will. Generally, he spoke half Latin and half Friuli; but by the afternoon Latin had taken up three-quarters of his conversation and towards night, after having drunk the decanter of the Ave Maria, he would give himself up entirely to Cicero. So also, if in the morning he would order a lenitive, in the evening he used drastic remedies only; and the leeches of the afternoon changed in the hours of the night to blood-letting. His courage increased with the hours and after supper he would have removed the brain of a madman in the hope that the operation might be successful.

No doctor of physics, no surgeon, no phlebotomist ever had lancets longer or more rusty than he. I believe that they were really lancets of the Huns or the Visigoths excavated in the ruins of Concordia; but he used them with singular skill so that in his long career he had only mutilated the arm of a paralytic, and his sole difficulty, though a frequent one, was that of stemming the blood, so large were the wounds he made. If the blood did not stop running with 'dragon's powder' he had recourse to the simple expedient of letting it flow, citing in Latin an axiom all his own: that no peasant had ever died unconscious. Seneca, however, was not a peasant but a philosopher.

Doctor Sperandio held the art of Hippocrates and of Galen in the highest esteem. And, indeed, he was quite right to do so; for, in addition to furnishing him with a living, he had made enough out of it to be able to buy a small house and a small estate near it in Fossalta. He had completed his studies at Padua, but named with a greater veneration the School of Salerno and the University of Montpellier; and in his prescriptions he paid great heed to simples which he found growing wild in the marshes and along the hedges, a most anti-Christian method that often put him at loggerheads with the apothecary of the district. But the doctor was a man of conscience, and since he knew that the apothecary himself extracted even foreign medicines from the local flowers, he revealed the fraud with the abominable simplicity of his remedies.

As regards social theories, he was a trifle Egyptian. Let me explain myself. He stood for the tradition of a profession in a family, and wished at all costs that his son should inherit his clients and his lancets. Signor Lucilio did not share this opinion, replying that the deluge would have been of no avail had it not washed away those mouldy doctrines of heredity tyranny. However, he bent himself to obedience and studied his five years in the most learned and ancient University of Padua. He was a scholar most notable for his idleness, who never made an appearance at the rare lectures, who was continually fighting with the gentlemen and policemen of the town and who at every snowfall always ran first of all to announce the fact at the Parlatorium of the Nuns of St. Croce. It was well known that whoever succeeded in this priority used to receive from the hands of the Reverend Mother the gift of a basket of fine pastries. Lucilio Vianello had emptied many of these baskets before obtaining his laureate.

But now arose the eternal question between father and son. There was no way in which the former could induce him to obtain this blessed laureate. Money for the trip there and back was put in his pockets, together with enough for a month's residence and the fee for the first examination. Lucilio embarked at Portogruaro on the postal boat for Venice; but he left, he stayed, he returned without money and without having taken his examinations. Seven times in two years was he absent in this way, sometimes for one month, sometimes for two, and the Professors of the Medical Faculty had not yet smelled his first fees. But what did he do in these absences? That was what Doctor Sperandio stubbornly set himself to discover, but to no result. After the seventh trip, he finally discovered that his noble son did not even take the trouble to reach Padua and that once in Venice he found himself so comfortable there that he did not dream of having to go further to spend his father's money. This the doctor eventually learnt from one of his patrons, a Senator, a certain nobleman Frumier, kinsman of the Count of Fratta, who spent the summer months at Portogruaro, and who also warned him of the suspicious behaviour of Lucilio at Venice and that the Inquisitors were keeping a paternal eye on him. Ipecacuanha! What more! Doctor Sperandio burnt the letter, stirred up the ashes with a spatula and looked askance at Lucilio who was sitting opposite him wiping some buffalo horns; but for a long time he spoke no more of the laureate. However, he took his son with him into his practice to try and discover the extent of his knowledge of the science of Aesculapius; and as he found himself satisfied with the results, began to send him about to look at the tongues

85

and the urine of the various peasants he had visited in the morning.

Lucilio opened a little notebook for the cases of Giacomo, Toni or Matteo, with a triple rubric for pulse, tongue and urine and, one after the other, as he made his visits, he filled these tables with requisite indications and reported in good order to his father, who was sometimes astonished at the violent changes and unexpected crises not usually associated with the maladies of ploughmen.

'What! Matteo's tongue clear and moist? Yesterday he was in bed with fever complicated by the putrid evil! *Putridum autem septimo aut quattuordecimo tantumque die in sudorem aut flexum ventris per purgationes resolvitur.* Clean and moist indeed! But this morning it was dry as tinder and coated two fingers deep. . . . Come, come . . . the Gaetana with a convulsive pulse! But only to-day I counted fifty-two beats to the minute and ordered her a potion *vinum tantummodo pepatum et infusione canellae oblungatum.* What does this mean? . . . Well, we'll see to-morrow! *Nemo humanae naturae pars qua nervis praestet in faenominali mutatione ac subitaneitate.*'

On the next day he would go and find Matteo with his tongue furred and the Gaetana with her pulse feeble, despite the pepper, the cinnamon and the wine. The cause of these miracles was that, on this occasion, Lucilio, not feeling inclined to make his round of visits, had compiled his own indications and filled in his rubric by guesswork in the shade of a mulberry tree. He had then handed it to his father to make him despair of his theories *de qualitate et sintomatic morborum.*

There were certain other occasions, however, when it was not so displeasing to the young man to have studied medicine at the University of Padua; when, for example, as soon as he arrived, Rosa prayed him to come upstairs to the old Countess, who was subject to nervous fits, and wanted to get from him a potion of laudanum and distilled water to calm her. Lucilio had for this almost centenarian old woman a reverent feeling compounded of love and veneration, and he could not give medicine and attention enough to maintain so worthy and precious a life. He would often stand and listen to her with an attention bordering on wonder, filled with delight at the words she spoke. Although of a secretive and reserved temperament, when talking with her he would warm to an involuntary candour and was not unwilling to speak to her about himself and his affairs as to a mother. Nobody, if he were to be believed, suffered as he did in being an orphan since the wife of Doctor Sperandio had died of childbed fever after bearing him, her only child; and he seemed to seek comfort in his loneliness in the feeling, almost as for a mother, inspired in him by Clara's grandmother. Little by little the old woman grew accustomed to him; she had him called even when she had no need of a doctor and listened to him telling her the news of the day with pleasure, finding him quite different from the other young men who frequented the castle.

Lucilia, indeed, merited this distinction; he had read much and had a great liking for history, and since he knew that every day is a page in the annals of the peoples, he followed with eager attention those first signs of disorder that were then to be seen on the European horizon. The English were at that time not too well regarded by the Venetian patricians; perhaps for the same reason that the bankrupt cannot regard with a kindly eye the new masters of his property. Therefore they always glorified the exploits of the Americans and the civil greatness of Washington who had liberated from subjection to the Lords a whole new world. The infirm old woman listened eagerly to his talk of events and of battles that always turned to the disadvantage of the English, and joined with him in a warm enthusiasm for that federal pact that had taken from them for ever the possession of the American colonies. When he spoke with pursed lips of the affairs of France, of the King's ministers who were being ousted one after the other, of the King himself who no longer knew on what party to rely and of the plots of the germanized Queen, she interrupted to tell him of the events of the times she had known: of the splendours of the court, the servility of the courtiers and of the proud and almost lugubrious solitude of the Great King, who had outlived the glory with which his contemporaries had surrounded him, only to assist in the frivolities and immoralities of his grandsons. She spoke with horror of the openly lewd customs which the new generation had begun to introduce, and thanked heaven that had protected the Republic of San Marco from the onset of this pestilence.

Once having left the Court of France for the Castle of Fratta she remembered Venice as it had been at the beginning of the Settecento, not yet unworthy of a place in the great council of European states; she could not know how much had happened in the meantime and with what flattering tinsel of elegance the indecencies of Versailles were now eagerly copied at the Rialto and in the palaces of the Grand Canal. When Clara read her some of the comedies of Goldoni she was scandalized and made her skip several pages; some volumes she had thought to take away and lock up. She could not have understood that what to her seemed barefaced impropriety of speech and licence of thought, created, in the theatres of San Benedetto or Sant' Angelo, the effect of a whiplash on customs even more impudent and corrupt.

Sometimes, too, she would touch on the reforms already begun by Joseph II, especially in ecclesiastical affairs; but the devout old woman did not know whether she should grieve at the humiliation of religion or console herself at seeing it carried out by such an enemy and antagonist of the Republic that he would surely be punished later by the hand of God. The Venetians had long felt, especially in the Friuli, the pressure of the Empire; and they had resisted it with force in the time of their military greatness and with prudent policy in the time of their continued civic wisdom, but now that both one and the other had been lost in universal indolence the more thoughtful contented themselves with relying upon Providence. That was reasonable for an old lady, but not for a governing Senate. Everyone knows that Providence matures her designs through our own thoughts, our own sentiments and our own works; and to hope to receive from her food already cooked was either a dream of the desperate or the flattery worthy only of street women.

Therefore when the Badoer fell into this childish hope, Lucilio could only shake his head; but as he did so, he bit his lips to hold back a smile that flickered at the corners of his mouth from under a pair of delicate and very black moustaches. I can wager that the reforms of the Emperor and the perdition of St. Mark did not displease him as much as he wanted to show.

The talk did not always concern such exalted topics; very often, indeed, it dealt with much nearer matters. In those times, steamships, telegraphs and metalled roads had not yet realized the great moral dogma of human unity, and every little group left to itself by the great difficulty of communications and almost complete judicial independence occupied itself almost exclusively with its own affairs, paying little heed to the rest of the world save as a subject for idle curiosity. The molecules had been divided from chaos, but there was not yet any centripetal force to weld them into other systems, interdependent upon one another and with reciprocal influences, both active and passive. Thus the inhabitants of Fratta lived, like the gods of Epicurus, in an enormous conception of their own importance, and only when some respite in their business or their pleasure allowed did they throw a curious or indifferent glance to right or left as occasion demanded. This explains why in the century just past there was such a lack of statistical information, while geography lost its way in accounts of strange customs and travellers' tales rather than revealing the real conditions of the world. This was the result of the capacity of the readers rather than the imperfection of means or the ignorance of the writers. The world for them was not a market-place but a theatre.

Frequently, therefore, these two would talk over the gossip of the neighbourhood; how such and such a commune had usurped the rights of such and such a feudal lord; how such a dispute was being argued before the Most Excellent Viceroy, what sentence had been given, or what soldiers or cavalry had been sent as a punishment to the said commune to eat up all its revenue. Future marriages were forecast and sometimes there was even a murmur of comment about those already established; and as a rule, the disputes, the oppressions and the discords of the signor castellans took up a good part of their discourse.

The old woman spoke of everything with sweetness and tranquil self-assurance, as if she judged from the standpoint of her great age and station; but this way of thinking was not always maintained and a good dose of simplicity and Christian modesty mingled with it. Lucilio played the part of a young man who enjoys learning from whoever knows more than he and with such discretion in a young wiseacre already seasoned with study, that he won more and more the esteem and affection of the old grandmother. Anyone who could have seen him adapt himself to her wishes and strive to render her every little service that she required, would have said that he was a real son to her, or was at least bound to her by the ties of some great benefit received. But this was not the case; it was indeed the effect of a good heart, of good breeding . . . and of design. For can you not guess? . . . I will explain in a few words.

When Lucilio took leave of the old woman to go down to the dining-hall or to return to Fossalta, she remained alone with Clara and never tired of praising the excellent manners, polite and educated spirit and wise discourse of this young man. Indeed his actions gave her material enough to sing his praises, like a mirror that seemed to reflect his inner excellences.

Simple and good-natured old women, when they take a liking to a person are wont to find in this one being all the tenderness, the care and even the illusions of all the loves that have been left alive in the fibre of their hearts. So I could not tell you whether a lover, a sister, a wife, a mother or a grandmother could have been bound to a man with stronger ties than the old Countess to Lucilio. Day after day he had known how to rekindle a flame in that aged soul, drowsy but not yet moribund, and finally she had come to love him, so that not a day passed without her wanting to see him and calling on him to keep her company.

Clara, for whom the wishes of her grandmother had the force of the law, had begun to want him also, and the arrival of

90

the young man was for the two women a great occasion. The Countess did not even suspect that the young man could think of anything else save to be kind to her, or perhaps to find pleasure in their conversation after the empty uproar of the dining-hall; Lucilio was the son of Doctor Sperandio and Clara the first-born of her first-born. If any suspicion had ever crossed her mind in this matter, she would have rejected it as a rash judgement and a dishonest and culpable thought, quite without justification for this pearl among young men. Let us say simply that she was too good and too aristocratic to harbour even the shadow of such a fear. Her affection for Lucilio was a real weakness and she became, as far as he was concerned, what she had once been for the little Orlando, when she had defended the liberty of his vocation. That she was not aware of the snare that had imprisoned the hearts of the two young people from the habit of seeing and talking to each other so frequently was not to be wondered at. Clara herself was not aware of it, and Lucilio used every art to conceal it. Do you understand me? He had sought the blind alliance of the old woman in order to conquer the young one.

I should be much embarrassed to guide you surely in the labyrinth of the soul of this young man and to say what portion in it was a virtue or a defect. His was one of those vigorous and fiery natures that have in them the seeds of all the qualities, good and bad, with the ever smouldering tinder of imagination ready to set them alight and the invincible reserve of an iron and calculating will to guide and correct them. At the same time more slave and more master of his own passions than other men, he was bold and patient, as one who esteems highly his own powers, but does not want to let them dissipate in vain; an egoist, generous or cruel according to need, who despised in others obedience to those passions of which he felt himself master and who believed that the lesser must always by Nature's law cede to the greater and the weak subject themselves to the strong, the coward to the brave, the simple to the cunning. Superiority, force, greatness of soul, shrewdness, he concealed them all in his knowledge of how to desire tenaciously, and to profit by all and dare all for the satisfaction of his desire. Of such a temper are those who do great deeds, whether good or evil. But how had he come to have, in his humble and circumscribed position, a nature so strong and tenacious, even if not in everything distinguished and perfect? I could not tell you certainly. Perhaps the reading of old historians and modern philosophers and the observation of society in the various communities where he had lived, had created in him a profound and haughty conviction. He believed that all men, great or small, must think in this way if they claimed the right to be called men. Great, such a temperament would have led him to command; small, it led him to despise others; two different sorts of pride of which I know not which would better suit the ambition of Lucifer. Everyone will agree that, if his spirit was lacking in that sensitive and almost feminine element wherein grows true kindness and pity, none the less a powerful intellect sustained him as he was, far superior to the humble destiny which seemed prepared for him by the circumstances of his birth and his more than modest condition.

His forehead, vast repository of great thoughts, seemed to rise even beyond the fine hair that shaded its summit; his deep-set brilliant eyes searched the souls and the hearts, rather than the faces, of men; his nose was straight and delicate and his mouth, firm and very mobile, denoted strong intention and secret and continuous internal activity. His stature was on the small side, as in the majority of great men, and his muscles, firm and elastic, served a body suited to his turbulent and active spirit. In all, he could have been called a good-looking youth, but the mass would have been able to find a thousand more handsome than he, or at least would not have picked him among the first.

A certain elegance, almost a foretaste of that English simplicity that was soon to take the place of fripperies and powder, regulated his manner of dressing; and that should have compensated for the lack of the prevailing fashion to make him conspicuous. He never wore a wig or used powder, even on gala days; he wore a round Quaker hat, knee breeches and highboots in the Prussian style, a doublet without ornament or enamelled buttons and a waistcoat in simple colours, either greenish or beige, not more than four fingers below his waist. These fashions he had brought with him from Padua and he said that they pleased him, as being more suitable to the country, as indeed was true. We, however, who were accustomed to the fripperies in the manner of Pantaloon, used to laugh at this simple and severe form of dress, without gold trimmings, fringes or bright colours.

The Pisana used to call Lucilio Mr. Blackbird, and when he appeared the urchins of Fratta crowded around him shouting this nickname in order to annoy him. He did not smile, like one who takes pleasure in the malice of children, nor did he get angry like a fool who takes account of it; he merely passed on his way, occupied with other matters. That was why we were so angry with him, and I believe that this air of indifference made him antipathetic to us, as his dress made him seem ridiculous. When, finding the Pisana, or even me, at the castle, he would smile at us and caress us, we enjoyed showing him that all his wheedling merely irritated us, and would run away, never failing to throw ourselves into the arms of whoever else happened to be there, or would begin playing with the Captain's hunting dog. Childish reprisals! But, while we avenged ourselves in this way, he would go on looking at us, and I still remember the impression and even the flavour of those looks. It seemed as if they were trying to say: 'My children, if I thought it worth my while to make you like me, I would do it in an hour.'

Indeed whenever he set his mind on anything, he succeeded every time. When I think back over the long way he travelled so constantly to get himself received into Clara's heart by means of the love and the praises of her grandmother, I cannot but be astonished. But he was always so; and I do not remember any enterprise whether large or small, on which he embarked, without proceeding therein with equal constancy, fair wind or foul.

93

The robust temper of this man, which did not at first invite my sympathy, ended by imposing on me that admiration which strong things merit in these times of universal flaccidity. More than that, his love for Clara, born and nurtured through long years of silence, protected by a thousand wiles of prudence and with all the internal fire of an invincible passion, had such an impression of sincerity that it redeemed other and less attractive sentiments of his soul. He always used shrewdness in his methods and perseverance in his ends, and if this was egoism it was the egoism of a Titan.

The old Countess, however, who saw in him nothing save what he thought suitable to show her, became more and more enamoured of him. The few other visits that she received during the day were not such as to diminish the pleasure of this one. The Signor Count, who used to come about eleven o'clock in the morning to ask how she had passed the night, before going to the Chancellery to sign everything the Chancellor put before him; Monsignor Orlando who, between eleven and noon, made a fourth with her kinswoman and her granddaughter, yawning widely in his desire for lunch; her daughter-in-law who sat by her for long hours, mute and rigid, knitting and never opening her mouth save to bewail the good old days; Martino, her late husband's major-domo, who kept her company in his own way, speaking little and never replying to the point, while Clara went out for her brief afternoon walk; the Pisana, who now and again was brought, with screams and scratchings, in Faustina's arms; these were the persons who passed before her every day with the monotonous satiety of characters on a magic lantern. It was not, therefore, strange that she awaited with impatience the afternoons when Lucilio came to make her laugh with his banter and to light up with a flash of gaiety the serene and grave countenance of Clara. When Lucilio perceived that his good humour which he instilled into the old woman passed also to the girl, and that she became accustomed to answer his smiles with others of her own, his patience began to hope that his reward was near.

Two persons who find pleasure in one another's company are

very apt to fall in love; the sympathy of two melancholy persons passes through smiles to the fervour of love and this joy has its own reason in the similarity that it reveals between our sentiments and those of another. Passion is in great measure formed of compassion. Lucilio knew that and more. Month by month, day by day, hour by hour, smile by smile, he followed with eager eye, enamoured but none the less tranquil, patient and sure, the increase in that affection that he was instilling into Clara's soul. He loved, but only looked; a new miracle of love. He saw the sympathy for the pleasure enjoyed by her grandmother in his company change into gratitude to him and thence into agreement for the praises which must always have been buzzing in her ears of his rare and brilliant gifts. Sympathy generated confidence and so desire, the pleasure of seeing him and speaking always of him.

So Clara began to smile of her own accord, as soon as the young man entered to ask the old lady about the state of her nerves and to take off his gloves to feel her pulse. This, as we have said, was for him the true beginning of hope, and he saw that the seeds had ripened and the young shoot was beginning to bud. At his first visits, too, Clara had smiled at him, but these smiles were different. Lucilio had a doctor's eye for souls rather than for bodies. For him the vocabulary of glances, of gestures, of accents, of smiles, had as many words as that of any other language, and he seldom erred in interpreting them. The girl was not aware of feeling in his presence any greater pleasure than she had felt at first but now he could always, without fear of error, send her a glance that could have said: 'You love me!' But he did not adventure such a glance while she was still unprepared. His will was master over him and backed by reason; passion, though powerful and tyrannical at its first onslaught, had still sense enough to confess itself blind and rely for its methods on these eloquent glances. Clara was devout; she must not be alarmed. Clara was the daughter of Counts and Countesses; one must not grope in her soul before having expelled all pride of birth. Therefore Lucilio halted at his first triumph, like Fabius Cunctator; perhaps also, since he

95

was very subtle in human relations, he enjoyed remaining for a while in that enchanting stage of love that has discovered that it is returned.

None the less, when coming sometimes from Fossalta he encountered the Fratta company returning from their daily walk and seeing Clara on the road, his cheeks would pale slightly. Not infrequently it chanced that the Partistagno was with her, proud of the honour, and while conversing with the others did not fail to turn upon the little Fossalta doctor a look of almost haughty disdain. Lucilio bore this look as he did the ridicule of the children, with an indifference even more proud and contemptuous. But that indifference showed only on his face; a hymn of victory sang in his heart. Clara's face, clouded at the sincere but crude gallantries of the young castellan, shone with a splendour of content when she saw from afar the grave and contemplative figure of her grandmother's adopted son. The Partistagno looked at her with a long glance of admiration. Lucilio scarcely glanced at her in passing. But both were intoxicated, the one with a vain hope, the other with a reasoned certainty of success.

As to the Signor Count, the Lady Countess and the good Monsignor, they were too involved in their thoughts or too occupied with their own greatness to pay any attention to such trifles. The rest of the company dared not lift their eyes so high, so these incidents went on between the three young people without incurring any profane or inopportune glances. Martino sometimes asked: 'Have you seen Dr. Lucilio to-day?' (He called him doctor even though he had no diploma, since he had looked at many tongues and felt many pulses in the village.) I would reply, shouting at the top of my voice: 'No, I haven't.' This dialogue always took place when Clara, either alone or accompanied by the Partistagno, went out in the afternoon, less serene and joyful than usual. Martino perhaps saw more than anyone else, but he never gave any other indication than this.

As for the Pisana, she often said to me: 'If I were my sister, I would marry that handsome young man who has so many

96

lovely ribbons on his doublet and so fine a horse with a gold-embroidered saddle-cloth; as for Mr. Blackbird, I would put him in a little cage and give him to Grandmother as a present on the day of the wedding.'

97

# III

The first time that I escaped from the kitchen of Fratta to wander in the outside world, it seemed to me beautiful beyond all measure. Comparisons are always odious; but I cannot therefore help making them, if not with my mind, at least with my eyes; and I must confess that, between the kitchen of Fratta and the outside world, I did not hesitate a moment to give the palm to the latter.

In the first place, Nature prefers light to darkness and the sun in heaven to flames in a chimney-place; secondly, in this world of grass, of flowers, of jumping and somersaults, there were neither the formidable scarlet trappings of the Signor Count, nor the rebukes of Monsignor about the Confiteor, nor the persecutions of Fulgenzio, nor the little-welcomed caresses of the Countess, nor the cuffings of the chamber-maid. Finally, though I lived in the kitchen as a vassal, two paces outside and I felt myself master and could breathe at my ease, even sneeze and say to myself: 'Your health, Excellency,' and reply: 'Thank you,' without anyone finding so much ceremony unseemly. The compliments received by the Count on the momentous occasions of his sneezes had always been a source of envy to me since I was a very little boy; for it seemed to me that a person who was wished so many good things must be of great importance and infinite merit. As I advanced in life, I corrected this unusual opinion; but so far as the feeling is concerned, I cannot even now sneeze in peace but there swarm within me desires to hear myself wished long life and happiness by a chorus of voices. Reason becomes mature and grows old; but the heart remains boyish and must be schooled with boxes on the ear in the patriarchal manner of the Rector of Teglio. As for the education that has now become the fashion, our hearts have very little to gain and much to lose in the exchange of sentimental banknotes that are now currency, for the true ring of the metal of times past. It is an education of artifice and

98

fraud, with no advantage to the cause of good since, according to the old saying, the greater always includes the less. But to return to the world which, as I have said, had at first acquaintance seemed so beautiful to me, I can assure you that it was, after all, no terrestial Paradise.

A small wooden bridge over the moat behind the castle led from the small courtyard of the stables into the vegetable garden, where two pergolas of knotted vines, laden in autumn with lovely golden clusters, were courted by all the wasps of the neighbourhood. Beyond were green waving fields of beet and maize which ended finally at a low surrounding wall, battered and tumbledown, and beyond this again vast rolling meadows filled with silver rivulets, flowers and crickets! Such was the world behind the Castle of Fratta. As to what extended in front of the castle, or on either side, I had to content myself with making its acquaintance at a later date; they kept me so tight on the chain with their Fulgenzio, their Rector and their spit that I had to enter the world of fresh air, the great temple of Nature, by escaping down the back stairs. But now a digression with regard to the spit, which has been for some time a load upon my conscience.

In the Castle of Fratta everyone had his daily task, save for the turnspit, who only carried out his on solemn occasions. It was not considered seemly to disturb him for the customary two chickens. So, while His Excellency the Turnspit enjoyed his silent and dusty ease, I was the turnspit. . . . The cook placed the two chickens on the spit, passed one end of it into a hole in the andirons and then gave me the handle, so that I should turn it with close attention and isochronous constancy until the victims had turned a rich golden brown. The sons of Adam, perhaps even Adam himself, had often done so; and I, as a son of Adam, had no right to complain of the duties entrusted to me. But how many things are done, said and thought without due consideration of one's rights! At least, so it used to seem to me for, since there was an enormous roasting-jack on the hearth, it was a bitter wrong to turn me into a roasting-jack. Was it not a sufficient martyrdom for my teeth that of all

99

this infernal roast I was only permitted, later, to chew and lick the bones, without also making me scorch my face, turning this way and that, this way and that, in an infinity of boredom?

Sometimes I had to turn a spit laden with tiny birds which, when their feet turned upwards, at every turn drooped upon the coals their tiny flayed and bloodstained heads. My own head nodded in rhythm with theirs, and I believe that I would have liked to change places with one of those chaffinches, so as to have my revenge on my tormentors by sticking in the throat of whoever was destined to eat me. While these sad little whimseys rasped my heart, I would laugh with a malicious joy and begin to turn the spit in greater haste than ever. But the cook would come clattering up and, pounding my hands, cry out: 'Slowly, Carlino, slowly. Small birds must be treated with care.' If anger and fear had allowed me to speak, I would have asked this greasy old woman why Carlino too should not be treated as least as well as a chaffinch.

The Pisana, whenever she knew that I was on duty as a roasting-jack, conquered her dislike of the kitchen and came to enjoy my rage and humiliation. Ah, what would I not have given this brazen little coquette for each one of her sneers! But none the less I had to swallow some bitter mouthfuls, and turn my spit, while an almost malevolent fury filled my heart and made me grind my teeth. Martino would sometimes, I believe, have relieved me, but the cook would not allow it, and indeed the good fellow had enough to do with his crusts of cheese and his grater. Moreover, when the soup began to boil, I had finally to endure the consolations of Monsignor who, angered at seeing me with tearful or drowsy eyes, suggested in his mellifluous voice that I should stop playing the clown or the naughty boy, and instead commit to memory the last part of the Confiteor until I understood it perfectly. But enough of all that; only to think of it, I still feel running down my back the juicy sweat of all those roasts, and as far as Monsignor is concerned, I would willingly send him where he has already been for some time, had I not greater respect for the memory of his quondam red stockings.

100

The world, however, had for me this last and most striking advantage over the kitchen of Fratta, that there I was not condemned to the martyrdom of the spit. When I was alone, I leapt, I sang, I talked to myself and laughed with the joy of feeling myself free, and began to study some fine gesture in the manner of the Pisana in order, later, to find favour with her. When I succeeded in dragging my enchantress with me over the furrows and through the thickets, it seemed to me that I had all that I could desire or that she could have desired. There was nothing that I did not consider to be mine or which I did not think I could get to content her; she was mistress and lady in the castle, but here in the countryside it was I who felt myself master and did the honours as if it were my patrimony.

From time to time, to make me conscious of my rags, she would say with a serious little frown: 'These fields are mine and that meadow is mine.' But to such childish assumptions of feudal rights I paid no attention whatever. I knew and felt that I had a mastery over nature not conceded to her: the mastery of love. I felt the same indifference as Lucilio felt for the haughty glances of the Partistagno and the ridicule of the village brats, for these regal airs of the Pisana. Once far from the battlements and the smells of the Chancellery, there boiled up in my heart that feeling of equality with which a sincere and courageous nature can look down upon even the heads of kings. I was the fish put back into the water, the bird escaped from its cage, the exile restored to his homeland. I felt such richness of joy that I looked for the chance of sharing it; and in default of friends, I could have made a present of it even to strangers or to those who wished me ill. Fulgenzio, the cook and even the Countess could have had their share of air, of sun, had they come to ask it of me nicely, without trampling my hands or tanning my backside. The Pisana followed me on my country escapades willingly enough when she could not find in the castle her little troup of retainers whom she could force to obey her.

In such cases she had to content herself with me and since she had often shown me the pictures in Clara's Ariosto, it did

101

not displease her to be either Angelica followed by Rinaldo, or Marfissa the unstained virgin, or even Alcina who enchanted and ensorcelled the captain of the island. For my part, I chose the role of Rinaldo with resignation enough, and fought fierce battles against rows of poplars which became dragons, or countered the desperate feats of some treacherous magician, bearing my ladylove behind me as if on the crupper of a horse. Sometimes we pretended to be taking long voyages, to the Kingdom of Cathay or the Republic of Samarcand; but we created terrible obstacles to be overcome, some hedge that must be a forest, some dyke that was a mountain, some brook that became a river or torrent. Then we used to comfort one another with brave gestures or took counsel with hushed voices, wary eyes and bated, half-stopped breath. At last we would decide to try our fortunes; down, therefore, at breakneck speed through puddles and ditches, leaping and shouting like two demons. The obstacles were not insuperable, but not seldom the little girl's clothes suffered some damage or she got her feet soaked paddling in the water in her little brown leather shoes. As for me, my jacket was an old familiar of the thorns, and I could have stayed in the water for a hundred years before the damp seeped through the calloused soles of my feet. It was therefore my part to console her, to repair the damage and to dry her when she got a little sulky after such misfortunes; whenever she did not begin to cry, or to start scratching me, I would make her laugh by taking her on my shoulders and leaping with her over ditches and brooks. I was as strong as a young bull and the pleasure I felt when she leant her face against my neck in order to have her hands free to sport with greater ease, would have given me wind enough to have reached, with this precious burden, if not to Cathay or Samarcand, at least to beyond Fossalta.

Wasting in this way the early hours of the afternoon, we began to range further and further from the immediate vicinity of the castle and to become familiar with other roads and paths and more distant retreats. The downland meadows where our first excursions took place sloped westward towards a fine

102

stream of water which meandered over the plain under great rows of poplars, alders and willows, like some peasant girl who had time to waste and little will to work. Under them there was always the sound of the perpetual twittering of little birds; the grass grew thick and very high like the carpet in the most secret chamber of some lady of fashion. The winding tendrils of creepers surrounded us amongst the thorny bushes and perfumed shrubs, and seemed to prepare for us the shadiest of retreats and the softest of couches for the games of innocence and the colloquies of love. The murmur of the water made more harmonious the silence and redoubled the enchantment of pure, fresh and silvery voices.

When we sat down on the greenest slopes to recover our breath, some green lizard would scuttle to the edge of a nearby thicket whence it would turn to look at us as if wishing to ask us something or to spy out our doings. For these pleasant respites we nearly always chose a bank of the river where, after a labyrinth of murmurous and capricious windings, it ran straight for a while, still and silent, like some madcap who all of a sudden had become a nun. The gentleness of the slope calmed its violent course, but the Pisana used to say that the stream, like her, was tired of using its legs and that we should imitate it and sit down for a while. But you will hardly believe that the little coquette would remain quiet for long. After giving me a few caresses or taking part for a while in my games, according to her mood, she would rise to her feet, unheeding and forgetful of me as if she had never known me, and lean out over the water to look at her reflection, or splash on it with her arms, or search the bushes for snail shells to make herself bracelets and collars, without heeding whether her sleeves or scarf trailed in the water. I would call her and tell her to be careful, more for the delight of having her once more playing beside me than out of respect for her clothes, but she would not even give herself the trouble to reply. Capable of falling into despair if a fold of her little collar was crushed when she condescended to join in the caprices of others, she would have broken or torn anything, even to her beautiful long black hair,

103

her round and rosy cheeks or her plump little hands, if the caprices to be satisfied were her own.

Sometimes, for the whole of the rest of our ramble, I could not succeed in rousing her from her grave, solitary and endless games. She would insist for a whole half hour in trying to make a hole with her teeth or nails in a snail shell in order to hang it on her ear, and if I made a move to try and help her, she would protest vigorously, stamping her feet, almost weeping and hitting me in the stomach with great strokes of her elbows. It seemed as if I had done her some great wrong, but it was all a caprice of her humour. Volatile as a butterfly which cannot remain for two seconds on the corolla of a flower without beating its wings to search out another, she passed in a single moment from gentleness to moroseness, from the noisiest chatter to an obstinate silence, from gaiety to anger, even to cruelty. The truth was that in all the phases of her moods her temperament never changed; she remained always the little tyrant of Fratta, capable of giving joy to some at one moment in order to try her powers and at the next to anger another, and make him cry, in some other experiment.

In sudden and sensual natures, caprice becomes a law and egoism a system, if they have not been chilled by a careful preventive education that arms the reason against the continual effort of their excesses and diminishes the sensibility with a barrier of good habits that acts as a refuge against the surprises of instinct. Otherwise, however many excellent qualities are innate in such natures, no one will rely upon them and they remain the slaves of sensual insolence. The Pisana was at that time a little girl, but what are girls but the buds of women? Whether painted in oils or on a miniature the features of a portrait remain ever the same.

But the new horizons now opening before my spirit afforded it a refuge against the petty tyranny of these first childish griefs. I found peace in the great bosom of Nature and her beauties diverted me from the melancholy company of my angry thoughts. That vast countryside where I then wandered was very different from the narrow limits of the vegetable

104

garden and the fishpond that from the age of six up to that of eight had given me so much pleasure. If the Pisana deserted me to caress or torment other small boys, or if she ran off half-way through one of our trips in the hope that in the meantime something had happened in the castle, I no longer ran after her to make a show of my miserable face and bowed shoulders; I went instead to forget my cares in the freshness of the fields or on the banks of the rivulet.

At every step there were new prospects and new marvels. I found a spot where the water widened out almost into a little lake, limpid and silvery as the face of a mirror. The lovely tresses of the water weeds mingled in it as though caressed by a magic zephyr; and the pebbles at the bottom shone white and polished like pearls that had escaped from their shells. The ducks and geese fluttered on the banks or suddenly all leaped tumultuously into the water and, after a momentary disturbance, swam in calm and intricate order like a fleet manoeuvering. It was a delight to see them advance, recede, turn hither and thither, without the transparency of the water being disturbed by more than a faint ripple, which died away at the water's edge in a still lighter caress. All around were dense thickets of trees on whose trunks the wild grape-vine wove countless green and capricious decorations; it would crown the summit of some elm and then abandon itself to the support of an oak, embracing it on all sides and falling in delicate festoons; from branch to branch, from tree to tree, it wove its way as if dancing and its tiny black clusters invited the starlings to a feast and the doves to quarrel with them for their share.

Just above this open space, where the little lake became a stream, two or three mills had been built, whose wheels appeared to run backwards, wildly splashing the water in every direction. I would stay there for hours watching it and throwing pebbles into the cascades of water, to see them bounce back once more and disappear under the giddy turning of the wheels. One could hear from within the rumble of the millstones and the singing of the millers, the shouting of the boys and finally the rattle of the chain on the hearth as they were stirring the

105

polenta. I used to watch the smoke that began to plume up-wards from the chimneys of the house and always preceded the entry of this new sound into the universal orchestra.

On the flat space before the mills was a continual piling up of sacks and confusion of flour-covered figures. The good wives from all around used to gather there and chatter with the women of the mills while their grain was being ground. In the meantime, the little donkeys, freed from their pack-saddles, fell gluttonously on the bran which was kept for them as a reward for their trip to the mills; when they had finished they used to bray with joy, stretching their long ears and legs; the millers' dogs barked at them and ran round them making a thousand feints of attack and of derision. It was a very ani-mated scene and I at least wanted nothing better, since in my whole life I knew nothing else save what had come my way in the tales of Martino, master Germano or Marchetto. Now, however, I was beginning to see with my own eyes, to reason and to learn with my own mind; to know what work and trade meant; to distinguish the various duties of the housewives, the peasant women, the millers and the donkeys. These things occupied me and entertained me; and I turned towards Fratta with my head in the clouds, watching the beautiful colours which varied according to the shifting mastery of the light.

My wanderings became ever longer and longer, and longer and more daring my desertions from the custody of Fulgenzio and from the Rector's school. When I had gone around on horseback with Marchetto, I had been too small to be able to imprint on my memory what I saw; and when I grew bigger, he did not want to risk taking me on the crupper of a nag who was too old in intelligence to be strong in the legs. So every-thing seemed to me new and unusual; not only the mills and the millers, but the fishermen with their nets, the peasants at their ploughing, the shepherds with their flocks of sheep and goats, and all, all gave me material for wonder and delight. Finally the day came when I thought I had lost my head or had fallen into the moon, so marvellous and incredible seemed to me the things I had before my eyes. I want to speak of it,

106

for that adventure confirmed for me, perhaps for ever, that simple and poetic religion of Nature which has since consoled me in every human sorrow with the sweet and never changing quietude of its joys.

One afternoon the Pisana was expecting a visit from three of her cousins, children of one of the Count's sisters, married to an up-country castellan. That afternoon, therefore, she slighted me so often and exposed me with such barbarity to the scorn of her cousins that she made me run away in a state of extreme fury, my only wish being to put as great a distance as possible between her and myself. I went out by the little bridge near the stables and off hotfoot across the sown fields, with anger at my humiliation riding at my back. I walked and walked with my eyes in the soles of my feet, heedless of everything, and when at last I came to raise them, I found myself in a place entirely unknown to me. I stood for a moment without being able to think, or better without being able to free myself from those thoughts that had up till then been hammering in my mind.

'Is it possible,' I thought when I had finally managed to shake them off, 'is it possible that I could have walked so far?' I was quite certain that the place where I now was did not belong to the usual circle of my wanderings; step by step I went back over all the territory that stretched for two miles behind the castle, sure that I had made no mistake. This, however, was a sandy and deserted spot, that sloped down into a canal, muddy and stagnant; on one side a meadow invaded by rushes stretched as far as the eye could see, and on the other sloped a badly cultivated countryside, in which the lack of order and apparent sterility contrasted sharply with the rank exuberance of a few large trees in irregular rows. I looked around me and could see no familiar landmark.

'*Capperi!* This is new!' I said to myself, with the satisfaction of a miser who discovers a treasure. 'Let's go on a bit and see.'

But there was a difficulty to be overcome in going forward, the wide canal, marshy and entirely covered with a lovely carpet of weeds and rushes. The vast meadow, with the unknown and the infinite, stretched away on the further side; on this side there was nothing but the arid and abandoned countryside, which did not attract me in the least. I was too spurred by curiosity to go back and too heedless to fear that the canal might be deeper than I thought. I rolled up my breeches to my thighs and descended into the water, using my hands and feet to clear the reeds and water lilies that encumbered it. Pushing on this side and pulling on that, I made my way through this floating forest, but the way sloped always downwards and the soles of my feet slithered over mud slippery as ice. When God wills, the bottom will commence to rise, I thought, and banished all fear from my mind; but I believe that I was so eager to go on that I would not have been able to turn back even had I drowned. Once I set foot on the grass I seemed to fly like a bird; the meadow rose slowly and it was already late when I had reached the highest spot whence I could look out over all my great conquest. I reached it at last, but so out of breath that I felt like a dog after coursing a hare.

As I looked around, I will always remember my astonishing pleasure, almost my bewilderment at the marvels that I saw. In front of me was a vast, grassy, flowery plain, intersected by great canals similar to the one I had already crossed, but even wider and deeper. They went on until they lost themselves in a stretch of water considerably larger still; and beyond this rose here and there a number of hummocks, some of them crowned by campaniles. But further yet my eye could not divine; what was that infinite stretch of blue, which seemed like a piece of the sky that had fallen and shattered upon the earth; a transparent blue, variegated with streaks of silver, which merged far, far away in the distance into a blue paler than the sky?

It was the last hour of the day; from that I understood that I must have walked very far. The sun at that moment, as the peasants say, turned backward, that is, after having declined behind a dense cloudbank, found close to the horizon a space whence to send to the earth a last glance, the glance of a dying man from under a lowered eyelid. Suddenly the great canals and the great lake into which they ran became a sea of fire, and that distant mysterious azure changed into an immense flashing mass with an infinity of varied and vivid colours. The flaming sky shone reflected in this mirror and every moment the spectacle grew in intensity, became more beautiful before my eyes, and assumed the ideal and almost impossible appearance of a dream.

I fell on my knees, as Voltaire on the Grütli when he avowed before God the sole article of his creed. God came into my mind also: the great and good God that is in nature, father of all and for all. I adored, I wept, I prayed; and I must confess that my soul, when later ravaged by greater tempests, often took refuge in the childhood memory of that moment in order to attain some ray of hope. No, it was not the repetition of the Act of Faith taught me by dint of much ear pulling by the Rector of Teglio; it was a fresh impulse, spontaneous and with all the vigour of a new faith which had been sleeping quietly, quietly, within my heart and which now suddenly awoke at the invitation of nature! In that universal beauty, I experienced a foretaste of the sentiment of universal good; I believed thenceforward that, even as the spring storms could not spoil the universal harmony of creation, so human passions would never be able to obscure the wondrous serenity of eternal justice. That justice is around us, above us, within us. It punishes us and rewards us, it alone is the great unifier of all those things that assure the happiness of the soul within the greater soul of humanity. Ill-defined sentiments that may at some time become ideas; but from the hearts wherein they are born illuminate the souls of men, and mine also; poetic sentiments indeed, but of that poetry that lives and becomes incarnate, line by line, in the annals of history; sentiments of a soul tried by the hazards of life, but which lie dormant in that sense of happiness and of religion, made me, a boy, bend my knee before the majesty of the universe.

Alas for me, if I had then thought of these high and almost

inexpressible matters! I would have racked my brains with philosophy and certainly would not have returned to Fratta that night. Instead, when darkness began to fall and the marvellous spectacle grew dark before me, I became once more of a sudden a boy, and almost burst into tears, fearing that I would not be able to find my way back to Fratta. I had run in coming; in returning, I ran even faster till I had reached the passage over the canal on which the sun still shone. But when I tried to make my way back over the countryside, the situation had greatly changed; night had already fallen, misty and very dark, and I who had come so thoughtlessly no longer knew how to find my way. I began to feel a feverish trembling and an impulse to run in order to arrive I knew not where. It seemed to me that however much I might have strayed on my way thither, I should have been able to return more rapidly by running than by my slow approach; but my calculations were at fault since my haste made me overlook those landmarks which could at least have assisted me not to lose my sense of direction. Also fatigue slowed my steps and I was too obsessed with the thought of not being able to reach home to persuade my legs to bear me onward.

It was mere luck that I moved sufficiently straight not to wander into the marshes where I should certainly have been drowned; and finally I came upon a road. But what a road! My God! To-day one would no longer dignify it with such a name. One would call it a deathtrap or worse. None the less I thanked Providence for it, and was able to walk more calmly, guessing reasonably enough that I should be able to ask my way at the first house I came to. But who could have been stupid enough to build a house in these marshy hollows? But I was confident and went on. The first houses would appear, sooner or later. I had not walked along this road for half a mile before I heard behind me the sound of a horse approaching at a gallop. I made the sign of the cross and huddled into the ditch as much as I could; but its pace was very fast and the horse, sensing that I was there in the shadows, shied violently, bringing from its rider a fine string of blasphemies.

110

'Who's there? Make way, scoundrel!' he shouted in a rough voice that froze the blood in my veins.

'Have pity on me! I am only a boy who has lost his way, and I don't know where this road goes,' I just found voice enough to say. My childish pleading voice must certainly have touched the horseman, for he reined up, even though he had just been spurring his horse on to ride me down.

'Ah, so you are a boy?' he said, leaning over towards me, and revealing a huge, dark figure wrapped in the folds of a great cloak, worthy of a smuggler or a wizard. 'Yes, so you are. Where are you going?'

'I am going to Fratta, if God wills,' I said, drawing back a little, fearful of this apparition.

'But what are you doing in these parts, where no living soul ever goes by night?' the unknown asked with some suspicion.

'I ran away from home,' I replied, 'and have been walking and walking, till I found myself in a wonderful place where I saw a lot of water and a lot of sun and many other beautiful things, though I don't know what they are; and coming back I got into difficulties because it was so dark and I did not remember the way, and now after running wildly, you see me here, and I don't know where here is.'

'You are behind San Mauro, near the pinewoods, son,' the man replied, 'and you are a good four miles from Fratta.'

'Signore, you are so good,' I began again, with more confidence, 'perhaps you could tell me how to get home by the shortest way?'

'Ah, so you think I am good?' said the horseman in a rather mocking tone. 'Well, perhaps you are right, and I will prove it. Get up behind me and, since I must pass that way anyhow, I will put you down at the castle.'

'I live in the castle,' I replied, not knowing if I should confide myself to the care of this unknown man.

'In the castle?' he exclaimed with surprise and displeasure. 'And to whom in the castle do you belong?'

'To no one! I am Carlino, who turns the spit and goes to school at the Rector's.'

111

'Not so bad; if that is so, jump up, I tell you; the horse is strong and won't even notice.'

Trembling a little and trying to reassure myself, I climbed on to the beast's back. The man helped me with one hand, saying that I should not be afraid of falling. In those districts one was almost born on horseback and one could say to any boy: get up on that colt! as one might say: sit on that rail. Therefore, when I had seated myself, he forced the animal to a frantic gallop that on such a road had all the dangers of a continual precipice. I held on with both hands to the chest of the horseman and felt the hairs of a very long beard gently tickling my fingers.

'Perhaps he is the devil,' I thought. 'He might well be!' And I made a rapid examination of my conscience, in which it seemed to me notable that I must have sinned more than usual to give him the right to carry me away on his horse. But I recollected in good time that the horse had been frightened of my shadow and since the devil's horses, according to me, should not have the weaknesses of ours, I gave myself a little peace on this score. But if it were not the devil himself, perhaps it was one of his lieutenants, some thief or assassin or who knows what else? But I had no fear of this. I had no money and felt that this was the best possible arm against any theft. So after having thought out what he was not, I began to consider what my nocturnal protector could be. Worse and worse! I defy the imagination of a Neapolitan to come to any more certain conclusions than mine and I had in the end to decide that I knew nothing. Suddenly the black subject of these fantasies turned his great beard towards me and asked in his usual and not very pleasant voice:

'Is Mastro Germano still at Fratta?'

'Yes, sir!' I replied with a start of surprise at this unexpected voice. 'He winds the tower clock every day, opens and closes the great gate and also brushes the courtyard in front of the Chancellery. He is very good to me and has often taken me to see the wheels of the clock with the Pisana, who is the daughter of the Signora Contessa.'

112

'Does Monsignor de Sant'Andrea often come to visit you?' he asked me again with a laugh.

'He is the confessor of the Signora Contessa,' I said. 'But it is some time since I have seen him because now, after I have begun to see the world, I stay in the kitchen as little as possible.'

'Bravo! Bravo! The kitchen is for the clergy,' he went on. 'Now you can get down, squirrel. We are at Fratta. You are the best horseman in the district. I congratulate you.'

'Surely,' I said, leaping to the ground. 'We always used to go on horseback, I behind Marchetto.'

'Oh, so you are that little parrot who used to ride behind him a few years ago,' he replied chuckling. 'Take this,' and he gave me a sharp blow on the neck, 'and give it on my account to the Serjeant; but since you are a friend of his, don't tell him you have seen me in these parts; don't tell either him or anyone else.'

As he said this, the man with the big beard forced his horse at full speed into a gallop down the side road that led to Ramuscello, and I remained where I was with wide open mouth listening to his horse's hooves growing fainter in the distance. When they had become only a faint murmur, I walked around to the moat and on the castle bridge saw Germano, who was looking around as though expecting someone.

'Ah, you little wretch! Ah, you rascal! Wandering about at such an hour! Coming home so late! Who taught you such tricks? Now, I'll teach you. . . .'

That was the manner in which Germano welcomed me; but the warmest part of his oration I cannot translate into words. The good Germano drove me in front of him with blows, from the gate of the castle to the door of the kitchen. There Martino jumped out at me:

'Little wretch! Gadabout! You won't do that a second time, I promise you. How dare you go out of the house at night and in such darkness . . .'

Here too words were the least part of my welcome, the most was the slaps that accompanied them. If I got this from my

113

friends, you can well imagine what I might expect from the others! . . . The Captain, who was playing 'goose' with Marchetto, contented himself with giving me a heavy blow on the back, saying it was all due to idleness and that they should hand me over to him to get good results out of me. Marchetto pulled my ears amiably; Signora Veronica, who was warming herself by the fire, turned to cap the blows of Germano, and that greasy old woman, the cook gave me a kick in the seat with such skill that I ended up with my nose on the roasting-jack that was turning.

'Just at the right moment! You are back in time!' the old witch cried. 'I have just had to put the roasting-jack into use, but now that you are here, there is no longer any need.'

With these words, she took the cord off the pulleys and put the spit in my hands after having taken it out of the jaws of the jack. I began to turn and turn again, not without being assailed and sniped at by the servants and maids as they came into the kitchen; and turning and turning once more, I thought of Gregorio, of Monsignor, of the Confiteor, of the Signor Count, of the Signora Contessa and of the nape of my neck. That evening if they had spitted me from end to end it would have done no more than diminish for me the martyrdom of fear. Certainly I would have preferred to see the nape of my neck well roasted rather than submit it to the hands of the Countess, and as regards tanning, I found that in my view St. Lawrence was more fortunate than St. Bartholomew. Since all were waiting to punish me, no one had been able to ask me what I had been doing during my long absence; but once I was pinned to the spit they commenced to bombard me with every manner of demand and question until, after having long stood firm under their battery, I finally broke into a flood of tears.

'But what's the matter with you, bursting into tears like that?' Martino asked me. 'Wouldn't it be better to reply to their questions?'

'I was down in the meadow by the mills; I stayed there near the water to catch crickets. I was . . . oh, oh, oh . . . it grew dark . . . and then I was late. . . .'

114

'And where are those crickets?' the Captain asked me. He had sometimes taken part in the criminal interrogations in the Chancellery and had picked up some of the tricks of the trade. 'I ...' I added in an even more tearful voice, 'I don't know. They must have escaped from my pockets! I don't know anything, I don't ... I was down near the water catching crickets ... I was ... ih, ih, ih ...'

'Attend to that spit, impostor,' shouted the cook, 'or I'll tan you ...'

'Don't scare him too much, Orsola,' Martino intervened, since he had guessed the meaning of her words from that old witch's face.

'Body of Pancrazio!' shouted the Captain, beating his hands on the table so that all the dishes laid for supper danced. 'Three times running those infernal dice must turn up a nine! ... That has never happened to me before! ... The game is ruined! ... That's enough; bear in mind, Marchetto! ... That's three bezzi I owe you from Sunday and two and a half to-day.'

'There are also seven from last week,' the Serjeant added cautiously.

'Ah yes, yes! Seven and five, twelve and a half,' replied the Captain, stroking his disordered hair, 'Just half a bezzo short of six soldi. I'll pay you to-morrow.'

'At your convenience,' said Marchetto with a sigh.

'As for you,' went on the Captain, turning to me in order to change the subject, 'as for you, little hypocrite of a turnspit, I'll soon deal with you. Isn't it true, Veronica, that I am famous at dealing with people?'

' Don't be silly! Do you want to send him quite crazy?' replied his wife, leaving the hearth and making her way towards the dining-hall. 'I shall go to the Signora Contessa and tell her not to worry any longer, since Carlino has returned.'

I did not have a mirror near me; but none the less I could swear that at this announcement my hair stood upright on my head like so many lightning rods. But I was soon brought to my senses by a fresh exhortation from the cook to get on with turning the spit and I stayed where I was, more stunned than

115

ever, to await developments. Indeed, I had not to wait for long. From the one side the Countess broke her daily rule and appeared for the third time that day in the kitchen with the Signora Veronica by her side, and from the other entered Fulgenzio, with his fat, smug face buried even more deeply than usual in the collar of his jacket. Never did the simile of Christ between the two thieves seem to me so appropriate as then; but at the moment I had no time to jest, since I knew very well that neither of those two thieves would have repented. The Countess advanced, tugging even more than usual at the hem of her coat, and stood directly in front of me; the hearth-fire made her eyes glow like two coals and the drop that only too often hung at the end of her hooked nose shone like a carbuncle.

'So,' she said, stretching out a hand towards me that made me shudder all over at the tremors that ran up and down my spine, 'so, ugly little toad, you repay the kindness of those who took you in, brought you up and even taught you how to read and write and to serve Mass? . . . I am sorry for you . . . I can see that your bad behaviour will drag you to perdition, that you will live an evil life, like your father, and that you will end up on the gallows, for in truth up till now you have always shown the right disposition for it.'

At this point I believed that I could already feel the tightening of the noose on my neck. But no! It was the fingers of the Signora Contessa which had fastened on their usual hold. I let out two screams so shrill that the Rector, the Chancellor, Clara, Signor Lucilio, the Partistagno and even, a moment later, the Signor Count and Monsignor came running out of the dining-hall. All these persons, together with those already in the kitchen, made up a very fine retinue of assistants at my passion. The spit remained still and the cook intervened to take my hands from the back of my head and set them to work again; but I was far too distracted at the furious actions of the Countess to pay any attention to any other matter.

'Tell me what you were doing, wandering about till all hours of the night,' she went on, putting, to my immense relief, both hands on her hips. 'I want to know everything, the

116

truth, the whole truth and don't tell me any more of your stories about crickets and don't blubber!'

The Signora Veronica grinned, as only wicked old women and the devil himself know how to grin; I for my part threw a glance at her that was worth a hundred curses.

'Speak up, little gaolbird,' shouted the Countess, waving her crooked paws over my head like the claws of a cat.

'I went for a stroll up to a place where there was a lot of water, and a lot of sun. And then . . .' I paused.

'And then?' asked the Countess.

'Then I came back.'

'Ah, then you came back and at what a time!' went on the Countess. 'I will show you whether or not you will have to tell me; but if you don't want to tell me what you were doing all those hours, I promise you on the word of a noblewoman that you will not taste the savour of salt again! . . .'

I remained silent; then screamed again because of another tweak at my neck from those monkey fingers of hers. Then I was silent again and began to turn the spit sullenly, since the cook had put the handle into my hands again.

'I can tell you, Signora Contessa, what this fine fellow has been doing,' Fulgenzio took it on himself to say. 'I was in the sacristy a few minutes ago cleaning the vases and the ampullas for Easter which is drawing near, and having gone out to the moat to get a little water, I saw coming from the direction of San Mauro a man on horseback who put down the signorino here and then said something to him which I did not quite understand. Then the man and his horse went on towards Ramuscello and the signorino went round the moat to come in at the main gate. That was how it was!'

'And who was this man on horseback? Was it you, Marchetto?' asked the Countess.

'Marchetto was with me all the afternoon,' broke in the Captain.

'Who was this man, then?' repeated the Countess, turning to me.

'It was . . . it was . . . nobody . . .' I stammered, recalling

117

the service rendered me and the warning given me by the unknown.

'Nobody, nobody,' grumbled the Countess. 'We will find out soon enough who this nobody was! Faustina,' she added, speaking to the 'children's woman', 'take Carlino's bed immediately into the little dark room between Martino's and the friars' guest-room and take him there as soon as the roast is finished. Out of there, my dear,' she went on, turning to me, 'you will not come until you have told us who this man on a horse was with whom you came as far as the Ramuscello crossroads.'

Faustina had picked up a light but had not yet gone to transport my mattress.

'Will you tell us who this man was?' asked the Countess.

I turned to look at Faustina and felt my heart breaking to think that, before going to bed, I would no longer be able to gaze at the Pisana, and even risk a kiss on the closed eyelids and dewy mouth. I thought perhaps that Faustina would not go.

'No, I saw nobody! I came with nobody! . . .' I replied suddenly with greater boldness than I had so far shown.

'Very well,' said the Countess, turning back to the dining-hall after making a sign to Faustina to tell her to go about the execution of her orders, 'let it be as you wish.'

She put her hands in her pockets and marched out, dragging behind her the whole band, like a retinue; but each of them before following her turned his eyes on me, sanctioning the just sentence of the lady castellan. The Count even exorcized me with a gesture that meant 'he has the devil in him'; Monsignor went on shaking his head as if he despaired of the rest of the Confiteor; the Rector pursed his lips as if to say: 'I understand nothing of all this'; and the Partistagno turned away gaily since he was bored with the whole affair. There remained the Contessina Clara, who despite the scowls of the Signora Veronica, of Fulgenzio and of the Captain, came up to me kindly and asked me if I had really told the truth. I looked around me and then answered yes, letting my chin fall on my breast. She then patted me kindly on the head and went out

118

with the others; but before she left, the Signor Lucilio came up close to me and whispered in my ear that I should stay in bed the next day and ask for him to be called in, and that in this way we should be able to settle the whole matter with little damage. I looked up to see if it were really he who was speaking to me with so much kindness; but he had already moved away, pretending not to notice a glance almost of complicity that Clara turned on him before moving away to the door.

'What did you say to that poor child?' she asked.

'I told him so and so,' replied Lucilio.

The young woman smiled and they returned together to the dining-hall since the hour for supper was approaching. They were followed by the Captain and his wife. There remained only Fulgenzio and the cook; but Marchetto and Martino liberated me from them, after making sure that the roast was finished, and advised me to go and sleep. Indeed Marchetto picked up a lamp and took me to my new abode by such long mazes of stairways and corridors that they seemed to me that evening to be unending. He arranged my pallet in a corner of the little room that was no more than a cupboard under the stairs, helped me to undress, and tucked the covers up to my neck so that I should not catch cold. I let him do all this, as if I were a corpse; and when he had left me and by the light of the little lamp left by him on a box I saw the battered walls and sloping ceiling of that cats' hole, desperation at no longer being in the gay, white room of the Pisana seized me so violently that I beat with fists and nails at my forehead and was not still until I saw my hands red with blood. In the midst of this frenzy I heard a soft scratching at the door and, most natural in a boy, my desperation gave place in a moment to fear.

'Who is it?' I said in a trembling voice through the sobs that still racked my breast.

The door opened and the Pisana, half naked in her little nightgown and with bare feet, trembling with cold, jumped suddenly on to my bed.

'You? . . . What are you doing here? . . . Why have you come?' I said, not yet recovered from my surprise.

119

'I came to find you and to kiss you, because I love you,' the little girl replied. 'I woke up when Faustina was taking away your bed and when I knew that they wouldn't let you sleep in our room any more, and that they had put you with Martino, I came to see how you were and to ask why you ran away to-day and nobody saw you again.'

'Oh my dear Pisana, my dear Pisana!' I began to cry out, holding her with all my strength to my heart.

'Don't make such a noise or they will hear us in the kitchen,' she replied, stroking my forehead. 'What's the matter?' she added, feeling her hand wet and looking at it in the moonlight. 'Blood, blood, you are covered in blood. . . . You've got a wound here on your forehead and it is pouring out! . . . What have you done? Did you fall or run into something sharp?'

'No, it is nothing . . . it was against the edge of the door,' I replied.

'Very well, so be it; whatever it was, let me heal it,' went on the Pisana.

And she put her lips to the wound, kissing and sucking it, as did the good Sisters of olden times to the breasts of their crusader brothers, and I went on saying:

'Enough, enough, Pisana; I am quite all right now. I can't feel that I ever hurt myself.'

'No, there is still a little blood coming out,' she replied, and again pressed her mouth to my forehead with such force as seemed impossible in an eight-year-old child. At last the blood was staunched and the vain little thing preened herself on seeing me so happy after her caresses.

'I came here in the dark, feeling my way along the walls,' she said to me, 'but down there they are at supper and I wasn't afraid that they would catch me. Now that I have cured you, I must go back again in case they find me on the stairs.'

'And if they do find you?'

'I will pretend to be walking in my sleep.'

'Yes, all right. But I am sorry that you are in danger of being punished by your mother.'

120

'If you are sorry, that makes no difference to me; it even pleases me,' she replied with a gesture of gratified pride, tossing her head to throw back from her forehead the loose hair that had fallen across it.

'You see that I like you more than all the others and when you have not got that filthy jacket on, as now, my Carlino, now that I can see you as you really are, I like you three times as much! Why don't they dress you in pretty clothes like my cousin Augusto had on to-day? . . .'

'Oh, I will get some nice clothes,' I exclaimed, 'I want them more than anything else!'

'And where will you get them?' she asked me in return.

'Where? Where? . . . I will work and make money and with money Germano says you can have everything . . .'

'Yes, yes! Work, work! . . .' said the Pisana. 'Then I will like you even more! But why aren't you laughing? . . . You were so gay just now.'

'Look and see if I am laughing,' I said with my lips on hers.

'No, I can't see you like that! . . . Further away! Let me see. I want to see if you are laughing! Don't you understand, I want to see you?'

I obeyed her and made a show of laughing with my lips, but in my heart I was thinking how much she would love me as soon as I could get those fine clothes.

'You are a dear and I like you,' replied the Pisana, murmuring in that little voice of hers that I still seem to hear and which still delights my ears in memory. 'Good-bye, Carlino, I kiss you and am going down now before Faustina comes back.'

'I must give you a light.'

'No, no,' she said, jumping off the bed and preventing me from doing likewise with one of her hands. 'I came in the dark and I will go back the same way as I came.'

'But I am afraid you will hurt yourself and will light you as far as the stairs.'

'Don't dare to move!' she said, changing her tone and leaving me free, as if sure that her gesture would have been enough to keep me still. 'Otherwise I shall be angry; I tell you

121

I want to go down in the dark! I am brave and fear nothing!
I want to go and I will go.'

'And if you fall or lose your way in the corridors?'

'If I fall or lose my way? . . . Are you mad? Or do you think
I was born yesterday? . . . Good-bye, Carlino. Thank me for
being good and coming here to find you.'

'Oh yes, I thank you, I thank you,' I told her, my heart
swelling with gratitude.

'Let me thank you too,' she went on, kneeling down beside
me and covering my hand with kisses, 'since you go on loving
me even when I am bad. Oh yes! You are really the best and
nicest boy of all and I don't understand why you never punish
me for all the nasty things I do sometimes.'

'Punish you. What for, Pisana?' I said. 'Get up now and
let me give you a light. You will get ill in this cold.'

'What?' exclaimed the little girl. 'You know very well that
I never get ill. Before I go, I want you to punish me. You must
pull out a big tuft of my hair for all the times I have been
naughty to you.'

And she took my hands and put them on her little head.

'Oh no,' I said, 'I would rather kiss you.'

'But I want you to pull out my hair.'

'And I don't want to!' I replied.

'What do you mean: don't want to? I tell you to do it . . .'
she began to shout. 'Pull out my hair, pull out my hair; if you
don't I shall scream so loud that they will come upstairs and
I shall get a whipping from mama.'

To quieten her, I took a lock of her hair in two of my fingers
and twisted it round my hand, playing with it.

'Pull! Pull out my hair!' she said angrily, drawing back her
head in such a way that I had to let my hand go with it for
fear of hurting her.

'I tell you I want to be punished!' she went on, stamping
her feet and pounding her knees on the stone floor which was
all rough and uneven.

'Don't do that, Pisana, you will hurt yourself.'

'Come on then, pull out my hair!'

122

I tugged very gently at the lock I held in my fingers.

'Harder, harder!' said the crazy little thing.

'Like this, then,' I said, tugging a little harder.

'No, not like that. Harder still,' she replied furiously. And while I still did not know what to do, she jerked away her head with such force that the lock of hair remained in my fingers. 'Do you see?' she added. And then, quite satisfied, 'That's the way I want to be punished when I need to be! . . . And now, till to-morrow, Carlino, and don't you dare to move or I won't go out with you any more.'

I stayed, astonished and motionless, with the lock between my fingers, while she slipped out of the door and closed it behind her; then I leapt up to follow her, but she had already disappeared down the corridor. I was certain that if her mother had torn out such a lock when punishing her, the child would have made noise enough to turn the whole castle upside down, and even to-day I marvel that she should have borne the pain without even blinking; so strong in her was her will and her fancy even from childhood. I do not know if those moments brought me more pleasure or regret. The courage of the Pisana in coming to find me through that dark labyrinth of the gloomy castle, despite the punishment that she might have received, had raised me to the seventh heaven; later her stubbornness had intervened to clip my wings, since I felt (I say felt, since at nine or ten years of age certain things could not yet be understood), I felt, I repeat, that the vainglory and vanity of displaying her prowess counted for more than affection in this proof of courage. I was therefore more than a little downcast after my first fervour of enthusiasm; and the lock of hair that remained with me remained rather as a proof of my servitude than of her good intentions towards me.

However, from my boyhood, the material signs of my joys, my sorrows and my various experiences were always very dear to me; and I would not have given up that lock of hair for all the fine gold and mosaic buttons and other extravagances that decorated the person of the Signor Count on ceremonial occasions. For me, memory has always been a book, and the objects that recall it at certain moments in my annals seem to me like those ribbons that one uses to mark the more notable pages. They fall immediately under one's eye and one has only to rely on them to find that point in the recital or that particular sentence that struck one, without needing to turn over the pages. I have always carried about with me for long, long years a little museum of trifles, of hair, of pebbles, of dried flowers, of knicknacks, broken rings, pieces of paper and other scraps that represent so many incidents, gay or serious, sweet or painful, but always memorable, of my life. This museum is always increasing and I preserve it with as much devotion as an antiquarian a rare medallion. If you, my readers, had lived as I have lived, I would only have to refer you to this long series of trifles and relics to recall to mind the whole story of my life, in the manner of the Egyptian hieroglyphs.

That lock of hair, uneven and tangled, that still preserves the marks of its tearing out, was like the first cross marked up to signify the passing of a day in the domestic shrine of memory. And it often later came into my mind to pray, to meditate, to laugh or to cry before this cross, from whose significance, mixed of joy and anguish, one could perhaps even then have prophesied the course of those events, sharp, confused and convulsive, that would later consume my soul and fortunately renew it. That lock of hair remains the A of my alphabet, the first mystery of my Via Crucis, the first relic of my happiness, the first word indeed recorded of my life, varied as it was and inexplicable as is that of all. Certainly, from the first moment, I realized its importance since it seemed to me then that I had no hiding-place secure enough in which to conceal it. I wrapped it up in a blank page of my missal and put it between my bed-covers and my mattress. A strange thing! So great seemed to me the inestimable value of those few hairs that they seemed to burn my fingers. I do not know if it were fear of losing them or of having them taken from me, or an instinctive perception of the tremendous promise that they later signified. . . .

I had already hidden them and lay very quietly pretending to be asleep when Martino arrived. Seeing me asleep, he took the light for himself and went into his own room. Then little by little the pretence of sleeping became a real sleep and this in turn became a fantasy of dreams, of phantasmagoria and transfigurations, which left me the impression of a whole life in that single night. Time is not to be measured as it would seem, by the swinging of a pendulum, but by the number of sensations. It could be so; and it could equally be that such a question is merely a juggling with words. I have sometimes in a dream lived long years and it seems to me that to explain this phenomenon one must compare time to distance and a dream to a steamship. Things seen are the same but they pass more quickly; distance is not so much diminished as devoured.

The next day I awoke with such a serious mien that I almost felt myself a fully-grown man, so long a time seemed to have been condensed into the last twenty-four hours that I had lived; and the memories of the previous day passed before me clear, ordered and vivid, like the chapters of a great romance. The scorn of the Pisana, the sneers of my pretty cousins, my humiliation, my flight, my reawakening on the edge of the canal, the perilous fording of that canal, the great prairie, my mounting on the hillock, the marvel of that stupendous scene of grandeur, splendour and mystery, the falling of darkness, my fears and my rush across the countryside, the noise of the horse's hooves behind me and the man with the great beard who had taken me on his crupper, the wild gallop through the darkness and the mist, Germano's whipping on my first arrival at Fratta, those other martyrdoms in the kitchen, the spiteful-ness of the Countess and my firmness, despite the dreadful punishment hanging over me, in not wishing to disobey the wishes of one who had rendered me a service, the caresses of Clara and the words of Signor Lucilio, my frenzy and the despair in which I went to bed, and the appearance in the midst of it all of the Pisana, a Pisana humble yet proud, kind yet cruel, thoughtless, capricious and yet very lovely as was her wont; does it not seem that all this would be too much for the brain of a child? And there in a sheet of paper under my pallet I had a talisman that during my whole life would recall

125

at my pleasure all that day so long and varied. Then recollecting the words of Signor Lucilio, I decided to profit by them and began to call Martino with all the voice I had. But the old man would have made me tear my throat to pieces before his eardrums would resolve to warn him of my cries, so I leapt out of bed and went into his room where he was just finishing dressing and told him I had a headache, that I had not closed an eye the whole of the night and that he should call the doctor as I was very much afraid I was going to die.

Martino told me that I was mad and that I should go quietly back to bed and that he would meanwhile go for the doctor; but first he went down to the kitchen to steal a little soup for me, an enterprise in which, protected by the darkness of the place, he succeeded admirably. I drank the soup with great difficulty since I had a burning desire for bread, and then retreated slowly under the bedclothes, promising that I would try and sweat. I believe that between the blows on my head, the exhaustion of fatigue and fasting and the sweat promised me by that hot soup, I succeeded in achieving a magnificent fever; so much so that when Signor Lucilio arrived in about an hour my hunger had passed and an intense thirst had taken its place. He felt my pulse, looked at my tongue and while he asked me about those scratches that disfigured my forehead, he smiled on me more kindly than at first, hearing in the corridor the rustling of a skirt. Clara then entered my mousehole to hear from the doctor the reasons for my illness and to comfort me by saying that the Countess, in view of my illness, did not insist on punishing me so severely and provided that I would tell her the truth about the evening before, she would even forgive me. I said that I had already told the truth and would have gone on repeating it; and if it seemed strange to them that I had wandered off in that way without knowing where I had passed almost an entire day, it seemed equally strange to me and I did not know what to do about it.

Clara then asked me about that place which was so marvellous and so full of light and sun and colour, where I said I had been; and when I repeated the description of it to her with all

126

the emphasis that I could, she said that perhaps Marchetto had been right and that I might have been at the Bastion of Attila, which was a height near the Lugugnana sea-coast, where the country tradition had it that, on coming from Aquileia, the King of the Huns had pitched his camp before being met by Pope Leo. However, from there to Fratta was seven good miles the shortest way and she could not understand how I had not lost my way on my return. And she went on to tell me that that most beautiful thing, immense, blue and of all colours, in which the sky was reflected, was certainly the sea.

'The sea,' I exclaimed. 'Oh, what happiness to pass one's life on the sea!'

'Indeed!' said Signor Lucilio. 'I have a cousin who has enjoyed this happiness for many years and is by no means so pleased with it. He says that water was made for fish, and that it was very foolish of the old Venetians to settle down in the middle of it.'

'It would be stupid now; but it wasn't at one time,' said Clara, 'when on the other side of the sea we had Candia, the Morea, Cyprus and all the Levant.'

'Oh, as far as I am concerned,' I replied, 'I would like to be always on the sea without bothering myself what might be on the other side of it.'

'But in the meantime, see that you keep well covered up and get well, little demon,' said Lucilio. 'Martino will bring you a little bottle from the apothecary's, as nice as jam, and you will take a spoonful every half-hour; do you understand?'

'In the meantime we will arrange matters with Mama as well as we can,' went on Clara, 'and since you have repeated that it was the truth that you told yesterday evening, I hope that she will forgive you.'

Lucilio and Clara went out and Martino with them, to go to the apothecary's; I remained with my sweat, with my thirst and with an overwhelming desire to see the Pisana, and it did not matter to me in the least then whether they forgave me or not. But the little girl did not appear and only in the courtyard I heard her voice and those of the other children twittering

127

over their games. And though I was afraid of being seen or prevented by Martino, I risked getting dressed and going down into the courtyard. I stood with ears strained and my heart in such a tumult that I could scarcely hear, till, about an hour later, I heard the Pisana shout up at the top of her voice:

'Martino, Martino, how is Carlino?'

Martino must have understood her and even replied to her, but I understood nothing; but I saw him come in a little later with the bottle of medicine, and he told me that he had met the Countess on the stairs and she had asked him if it were true that I had split my forehead against the wall for desperation.

'Was it true?' asked the good Martino.

'I don't know,' I replied, 'but yesterday evening I was so wrought up that I might have done all sorts of foolish things without remembering anything about them later.'

'You don't remember?' said Martino who had understood very little.

'No, no, I don't remember,' I replied.

He was not at all satisfied with such a reply, since it seemed to him that after having injured my face in such a way, I should have had the best possible recollection of it.

The medicine had its effect, however, perhaps better and more rapidly than anyone had anticipated, for I got up the same day; and as for the punishment threatened by the Countess, nothing more was heard of it. It was true, however, that there was no question of sending me back to Faustina's room and that my kennel remained finally next to Martino's room. As may be imagined, my desire to see the Pisana again, after the incidents of the previous night, played a major part in my unexpected recovery; and when I went down to the kitchen, my first thought was to look for her.

The family had only just finished lunch, and Monsignor, meeting me on the staircase, chucked me under the chin, contrary to his usual custom, and looked at the scars on my forehead, which by this time were no great matter. He said that I could not be the pest they believed me to be if the shame of being thought a liar had made me do such violence to myself;

128

but he advised me to use more discretion in the future, to lay my sorrows before God, and to learn the second part of the Confiteor. In the benign words of Monsignor I recognized the good offices of Clara, who had given the most edifying reasons for my folly, and thus, if not completely forgiven, I was at least conceded a complete oblivion. I learnt later from Marchetto that Signor Lucilio had described me as a very timid and moody boy, easily depressed in strength and health by any displeasure, and between him and Clara they gave such surety for my sincerity that the Countess did not like to accuse me of duplicity. Furthermore, she did not bother about interrogating Germano; but he, perhaps primed by Martino, volunteered that he had certainly heard the sound of a horse's hooves the night before, but some little time after my return to Fratta, so that it was quite possible that the horse had not brought me. So the testimony of Fulgenzio was left in peace and I too remained in peace and no longer had to tell lies owing to my scruples of conscience. None the less, I must add that what may appear to some to be the frivolous and determined obstinacy of a boy seemed to me then, and still seems to me, a good proof of fidelity and gratitude.

That was the first time my spirit had to struggle between pleasure and duty; nor did I waver a moment to hold to the latter. If the duty in this case was not very stringent, since neither had the request of the unknown been given very stringently, nor had I promised anything nor had I done any good by keeping silent about a fact so usual as the passage of a horseman by night, yet all that proves thricefold the rectitude of my sentiments. Perhaps also my first sacrifice, which I accepted voluntarily and for so idle a motive, gave to my nature a twist that I have not ceased to follow almost always in graver and more serious circumstances.

That afternoon, as I have said, my first care was to go in search of the Pisana, but to my chagrin I was unable to find her anywhere. I asked the maids who, as if caught in default for their carelessness about the little girl, were irritated by my insistence. Germano, Gregorio and Martino, whom I also

129

asked, could not tell me anything and finally in a fury I went to the back of the stables and asked the gardener if he had seen her go out somewhere. He replied that he had seen her go off into the countryside with the son of the apothecary, but that was already two hours ago and the little Countess must by now have returned since the sun was already high and scorching and she did not like to get sunburnt. I, however, knowing the crazy humours of the girl, did not believe this and went out too into the fields. The sun shone down scorching on my head and the ground crackled under my feet because of the heat, but I did not notice it because of the great mission that drove me on. At the edge of a ditch I found a pair of shoes. They were the Pisana's and I followed the trail convinced that my great desire would lead me to find her somewhere or other. I looked into the thickets and along the brooks and in the shade where we used to rest during our walks; I hunted everywhere, driven by jealousy, and if the little son of the apothecary had then fallen into my hands I would have given him a good beating without giving him a chance to ask why.

As for the Pisana, I knew her through and through and was foolishly inured to her ways. I had commenced to love her even because of her faults, just as a good trainer prefers amongst all his horses the one who rears and kicks the most and resists the spurs and the reins. There is no quality that makes a thing so dear and precious to us as that of realizing that it is always ready to escape us; and if such an attitude of fear and effort wearies weak spirits, it arms and strengthens the constant ones. It might be said that the Pisana had bewitched me if I could not read clearly enough the reason for this spell in the pride continually stimulated in me by my superiority over all her other pretenders. I saw myself preferred most frequently and above all the others, but I wanted to be so always.

As for the sentiment that made me want this, it was the purest and most unmixed love; love that later increased, that was for ever changing temper and colour, but which filled my soul with all its madness. And love at ten years old is so excessive, as is every other wish at that age of trust that does

130

not yet know what impossible means. Always in accord that here the paucity of words makes me say love in place of that other word, whatever it may be, that should be used. Because a passion so varied, that embraces the highest culmination of the soul and the lowest bodily impulses, that knows how to bow on the one hand in assent and to rise to the heights on the other, and confound them all sometimes in an ecstasy almost divine and yet sometimes almost bestial, should have twenty different names instead of a single generic one, devoted to good or to ill according to the occasion and chosen one might say on purpose to alarm the modest and excuse the unworthy. I therefore said love, and could not say otherwise; but every now and then when I have to use such a word in the course of my story, I feel obliged to add a line of comment to supplement our vocabulary.

At that time, therefore, I loved the Pisana as the companion of my childish games; and since at that age games are all-important, that means to say that I loved her completely; which, if it does not constitute that pure unmixed love which I have referred to above, you must take it up with the dictionary makers. Despite my frenzied search for her that afternoon she did not allow herself to be found, and searching here and looking there, I took without being aware of it the way that had led me so far afield the day before. When I noticed this I found myself at a country crossroads where on a low, rough stone wall a poor San Rocco showed the wound on his leg to the devout passers-by. The faithful dog stood by his side with drooping tail and his nose raised as if to see what his master was doing. All this I saw when I first raised my eyes; but on looking round, I also noticed an old bent beggar-woman who was praying with great fervour before that San Rocco.

It appeared that she was the Martinella, a poor beggar-woman so-called in the district, who used to stop and take her alms from Germano's box whenever she passed by the Fratta bridge. I spoke to her with a certain hesitation, since Marchetto's tales had made me suspicious of witchcraft in all old women; but the strength of my need pressed me on. She turned

131

an angry face towards me, though she was usually the most patient and amiable old woman of all the many in the neighbourhood; and mumbled questions as to what I was doing in that place and at that hour. I replied that I was looking for the Pisana, the little daughter of the Contessa, and that I was just going to ask if she had seen her pass with the apothecary's little boy.

'No, no, Carlino, I haven't seen her,' the old woman replied hastily and with irritation, though I had tried to show her every consideration. 'While you were looking for her she had already gone back to the castle another way. Go, go back to the castle. I am sure you will find her there.'

'But no,' I said, 'she only finished lunch just an hour ago.'

'I tell you that if you go there you cannot fail to find her,' the old woman interrupted me, 'only five minutes ago, now I remember, I must have seen her as she went back by the Montagnesi fields.'

'But I passed that way five minutes ago,' I persisted in my turn.

'But I tell you I saw her.'

'No, you can't have done.'

While I was reasoning with her and the old woman was doing her best to make me go back, we suddenly heard the sound of a horse galloping down one of the side roads. The Martinella left me standing there and with a shrug of her shoulders moved off to meet the horseman, as if to beg from him. The next moment the horse plunged out of the sunken ditch of the side road. It was a strong fiery colt with quivering nostrils and mouth flecked with foam. On it was a man, large and ragged with a huge grey beard blown to the four winds and a great hat, faded from the rains, over his nose. He had neither stirrups, saddle nor bridle and only controlled his mount with the ends of a halter which he used as a whip to make it increase its pace. At first glance he reminded me of the bearded man who had brought me home the evening before; and the suspicion became a certainty when he replied in a harsh and grating voice to the salutations of the beggar-woman. She turned,

132

glancing towards me, and he, having pulled up the colt near the old woman, leant down and muttered a few words in her ear. The Martinella at once brightened up, lifted her arms to the sky and then said aloud:

'God and San Rocco will reward you for your good action. And as for charity, I rely on you and will remember you at the end of the week.'

'Yes, yes, Martinella, don't fail me,' said the man, pressing his legs against the colt's flanks and dashing off at full speed on the road to the lagoons. When some distance away, he turned back to the old woman and made a sign towards the road from which he had just come; then horse and rider disappeared in the dust raised by its hooves.

I stood intent on this scene when, looking away from the spot where the horse had disappeared towards the countryside opposite, I saw the Pisana herself and the apothecary's boy who were running to me in a great fright. I began to go towards them when the Martinella shouted to me: 'Where are you going, Carlino?' I called back: 'There, there she is, the Pisana! Don't you see her?' I soon reached the little girl, but she was so pale and terror-stricken that she moved me to pity.

'But, Pisana, what is the matter? Are you ill?' I asked, taking her by the arm.

'What a fright I have had . . . what a rush . . . they are over there with their muskets . . . they want to cross the stream,' replied the little girl, panting for breath.

'Who are you talking about—who wants to cross?'

'There they are!' Donato, the apothecary's son, burst out in reply, recovering a little from his fright. . . . 'There they are . . . we were playing near the mill stream when four or five men suddenly appeared on the far bank with pistols in their hands— enough to frighten anyone—and they seemed to be looking for something and getting ready to wade across. And the Pisana ran away and I ran after her as fast as I could; but some of them started shouting: "Have you seen a man on horseback over there?" The Pisana didn't answer and neither did I and we went on running, and here we are; but the men will surely come

133

here for, even though the water is deep, the mill bridge is not far away.'

'Let's get away! Let's get away!' shouted the little girl, panic-stricken.

'Have courage, Signorina!' interrupted the old woman, who had been listening to all this. 'These Cernide are not looking for you but for a man on horseback; and when they come here Carlino and I will tell them that we have seen no man on horseback except the guard from Lugugnana going to look at the hay at Portovecchio.'

'No, no, I want to go away. I am afraid!' shrieked the little girl.

But there was no time to run away for four buli suddenly appeared and after looking down the four side roads turned to the old woman with the same question that they had just asked the two children.

'We only saw the guard from Lugugnana who was going to Portovecchio,' the old Martinella replied.

'Eh, what guard from Lugugnana? That must have been him!' said one of the band.

'Listen, Martinella,' asked another of them, 'don't you know the Spaccafumo?'

'The Spaccafumo!' exclaimed the old woman with horror in her eyes. 'That ruffian, that bandit, who fears neither God nor the law, as bad as a Turk! No, thanks be to God, I don't know him; but I saw him one Sunday in the pillory at Venchieredo about two years back.'

'And you haven't seen him anywhere around to-day?' asked the man who had spoken first.

'How could I have seen him to-day? They say he was drowned at the end of last year!' replied the old woman. 'And I must admit to you gentlemen that I suffer a little with my eyes.'

'Listen to that! Of course it was he!' exclaimed the man. 'Why didn't you say at first that you are as blind as a mole, old hag? Come on, don't waste any more time. To Portovecchio, brothers!' he added, turning to his men.

134

And all four set off by the road to Portovecchio which was in the opposite direction to that taken by the bearded man a quarter of an hour before.

'But they have made a mistake . . .' I began to say.

'Quiet!' whispered the Martinella, 'let those ruffians go away and we will say a Pater Noster to San Rocco who has rid us of them instead.'

The Pisana during the talk with the men had recovered all her courage and now seemed surer of herself than any of us.

'No, no,' she cried, 'before praying we must run to Fratta and warn the Chancellor and Marchetto about these horrible men that we have seen. Isn't it the Chancellor's duty to keep all evil-doers off papa's lands?'

'Yes, certainly,' I replied, 'and also to put them in prison if he thinks fit.'

'Then let's go and have those four nasty men put in prison,' she went on, dragging me towards Fratta. 'I won't, I simply won't have them frightening me again!'

Donato followed behind, left completely out in the cold by the capricious little girl; and the Martinella remained on her knees before San Rocco as if nothing out of the way had happened.

# IV

THE Spaccafumo was a baker from Cordovado, a picturesque
little district between Teglio and Venchieredo, who, having
entered into open war with the local authorities, had won the
award of such a nickname from the prodigious hue and cry
that they made in pursuit of him. (Spaccafumo, in the somewhat Venetianized dialect of the Friuli at that time, was
equivalent to 'dust-raiser'—sbattipolvere—but if I translated
his name so, it would almost seem as if I debaptized him; I do
not remember ever having heard his real name.) His first
venture was against the agents of the customs and excise, who
wanted to confiscate a certain bag of salt that they found at
an old woman's who lived in the house next to his. I seem to
remember that the old woman was the Martinella herself who
at that time, since she was still able to work, had not yet
begun to beg. Condemned to two years' banishment, the Mayor
of the commune, Signor Antonio Provedoni, had compounded
his punishment for a fine of twenty ducats. But after this
brush with customs officials over the bag of salt, he had got
involved in another with the Vice-captain of the prisons, who
wanted to imprison a cousin of his for having been found at
the Venchieredo festa bearing arms. He was then condemned
to three days in the pillory on the village square, with two
months' imprisonment and banishment from the district for
twenty-eight months. He then stopped making bread; but that
was all his obedience to the decrees of the Criminal Chancellery
of Venchieredo amounted to. He went on living here and there
in the countryside and exercising his ministry of private
justice for the good of the public.

The posse of Portogruaro had been unleashed upon him
twice; but he beat the dust at such speed and knew so well all
the hiding places and byways of the country that they had
done nothing at all towards catching him. As to surprising him
in his lair, that was a still more difficult enterprise; all the

peasants were on his side, and nobody could say where he used to sleep or take refuge in bad weather. Furthermore, if the posse of Portogruaro moved with too great solemnity ever to catch him unawares, the bravos and militia of the local magistrates were on much too good terms with the local peasants ever to try and pursue him seriously.

Sometimes, after nothing had been heard of him for weeks and weeks, he would appear quite calmly at the parish Mass of Cordovado; but he listened to the Mass with one ear only; the other he kept well cocked towards the main door, and was ready to escape by the side one if he should chance to hear the heavy measured tramp of a patrol. That they should ever be cunning enough to station themselves at both doors was not to be thought of, granting the perfect good faith of that militia. After Mass he would join some old cronies on the square, and at lunch-time went directly and openly to the Provedoni house, which was the last house in the village in the direction of Teglio.

Signor Antonio, the Mayor of the commune, closed an eye; and the rest of the family used to gather round him in the kitchen with great pleasure, to hear him tell of his prowess and to laugh at the jests with which he enlivened his tales. He had been on good neighbourly terms with that family since boyhood and he continued to be so, as if nothing had happened; so much so that to see him go there every so often to eat his bowl of 'brovada' in front of the fire had become a matter of habit with all of them.

The Provedoni family was of some importance in the country for its age and reputation. I myself remember having read the name of Ser Giacomo della Provedona in the records of a district gathering held in 1400, and from then on it had remained the leading family in the commune. But if the fate of the poor communes was not very gay in the midst of the castellans' jurisdictions, even shabbier was the standing of their leaders in the face of the feudatories.

San Marco was popular, but at a distance, and mainly for show; at heart it was too wishful to retain, more especially in

137

the Friuli, the homage of the nobility to want to raise up against them that scarecrow of the communal jurisdictions. They patiently put up with those already in existence, which were excusable so long as they did not give reason for being abolished by some too haughty insistence on their strict rights, but kept them in holy humility with a thousand restrictions and a thousand fetters; while as to establishing new ones, they never even dreamed of it. If a juridical office, for reasons of extinction, of sentence or of felony, reverted to the Republic, rather than reconstitute it as a commune it was the custom to invest its powers in some feudal magistrature, or as it was then termed, some provincial office. Thus there was achieved, without undue fuss, the double aim of restricting at least the number of the castellans, whose support was a necessity not always altogether desired, and of maintaining the population in their usual blind servitude, divorced as much as possible from public affairs. Moreover, if the communes in their disputes with the castellans were often in the wrong according to the letter of the law, they were always so before the courts; and that, incidentally, by the private connivance of the patrician magistrates sent year after year from the Serene Dominant to judge in the Supreme Assizes of the Terraferma. There was, however, one method to make all ranks equal before the sacred impartiality of the tribunals; and that was money. But if one considers the Italian love of litigation that clashed in the communes with the very prudent Friuli economy, it was easy to understand how very rarely they were disposed to look for and obtain justice by such means. The castellan had already paid his zecchino while the commune was still arguing about its farthing; these had already a favourable judgement in their hands while those were still squabbling about a clause in the reply or the duplicate.

Signor Antonio Provedoni was respectful to the nobility by sentiment, not servile by worthlessness. His family had always behaved in this way and he did not intend to change its customs. But this respect of his, sufficient but not profuse, made him looked on with a favourable eye; as things were then, not to make a show of cowardice was reputed as great valour of spirit. By that, I do not mean to say that he would resist the arrogance of the neighbouring castellans; he merely did not go to meet them with gifts, and that was much. He would, however, grumble to himself about this arrogance, a sign to his mind that the old nobility, a mingling of grandeur and courtesy, was tumbling into the abyss; in greed and oppression they were now almost comparable to the police. But never did one of these laments emerge from that silent and prudent mouth; he contented himself with remaining silent and bowing his head as the peasants do when providence sends them hail. The sun, the moon and the stars, he and his forbears had always seen them turning in the one way, whether the year was wet, dry or snowy. After a bad year had come many good ones and after a good year many bad ones; and a similar reasoning he applied to the things of the world. They were prosperous or adverse in their turn; he had lighted on a bad one, that was all. But he had great faith that matters would be better for his sons and grandsons; it was enough for him to have engendered them in good time, so that the family should not be defrauded of its share of happiness. Only the second-born of his numerous children, on whom he had been pleased to impose the name of Leopardo, gave him some cause for bitterness. But how could anyone be tame and docile with a name like that?

The good Mayor of Cordovado had behaved in this matter with somewhat insufficient circumspection; the names of his sons were all more or less ferocious and animal, far indeed from instilling in them the practice of those virtues of tolerance, silence and compliance that he knew were most suitable to men of their rank. The first was called Leone; the second, as we have said, Leopardo; the others were in order: Bruto, Bradamante, Grifone, Mastino and Aquilina. Indeed, a real menagerie, and Signor Antonio could not understand that, saddled with such names, the usual peasant good-humour became burlesque and impossible. If at that time, as in that of the Latins, they had dared to adopt the Christian name of Bestia, certainly his first-born would have received it in gift, so

x

enthusiastic was he for zoology. But granted the impossibility of putting into operation this generic name, he had replaced it with the even prouder and more menacing one of the King of the Beasts, according to Aesop. Leone, however, did not show himself less sheeplike than the times, or at least his paternal example, required. He had gone his way, supporting much, and sighing from time to time, and then, like his father, had taken a wife and begotten sons, of whom he had already half a dozen, at the time when Leopardo first began to take an interest in women. This is the point where we shall begin to treat of the family dissensions between Signor Antonio and Leopardo.

Leopardo was a young man of few words and many deeds; that is to say, of few deeds too, but in those few he was so obstinate that there was no means to dissuade him. Whenever anyone rebuked him, he would turn on them with a kind of roar deep down in his throat and with two eyes so baleful that the rebuker as a rule never got beyond his exordium. Otherwise, he was as good as bread and as useful as five fingers.

He worked in his own way for two hours every day and in those hours he would have defied the devil himself to employ him otherwise; the remaining twenty-two they could put him to cutting wood or planting cabbages or even turning the spit as I did and he would not even give a sign of annoyance. He was on these occasions the tamest leopard that ever existed. Intent on his own duties and assiduous in all that he did and at his rosary, he was in short a good Christian, as was usual in those times, and furthermore educated and learned beyond all custom of his contemporaries. But as regards logic, I have every reason to believe that he was a trifle obstinate. A racial merit, perhaps, but while the obstinacy of others was often hidden away in their conscience, leaving the rest free to outward compliance, he was indeed, so to speak, a mule inside and out and would have kicked in the face, I believe, even the Most Serene Doge himself if he had dreamed of opposing him in his fixed ideas. Laborious and vehement in all his actions, when inactive he became inert and leaden, like the wheel in a workshop when the strap has been cut. His strap was his conviction,

140

without which he would not advance even at a snail's pace, and as for allowing himself to be convinced, Leopardo had all the flexibility of a fanatical Turk. The reason for so much tenacity was perhaps that he had grown up in solitude and silence; the thoughts in his brain were not stiffened with the fragile joining of a graft but with the thousand tendrils of an oak root, that grows slowly before breaking into bud and bearing fruit. Over an exhausted and sterile graft another graft may grow, but roots cannot be uprooted, or if uprooted, dry up; and Leopardo had his head formed in such a way that it could not be planted on the neck of any save a great man or a madman. Either just so or nothing at all. That was the formal significance, the heraldic motto, of his nature.

Leopardo had lived happily up to the age of twenty-three without questioning or suffering questioning from anyone. The precepts of his parents and masters had agreed so exactly with his own views that he found no need to ask anything of them or they to demand anything from him. But the source of all his troubles was the spring of Venchieredo.

After he had begun to drink of the waters of that spring there ensued a hailstorm of questions, of counsels and of re-proofs from his father. However, since all these discourses in no way corresponded with Leopardo's views, he for his part took to roaring and scowling. Then, as Sterne would say, the bestial influence of his name took the lead; and if this were so, Signor Antonio's passion for beasts must have cost him dear.

Let us make this riddle a little clearer.

Between Cordovado and Venchieredo, about a mile from each of them, was a large and limpid spring which had the reputation of containing in its waters many salutary qualities. But the nymph of the spring did not rely solely on the virtues of her waters to allure her worshippers, but had surrounded her-self with such a beautiful horizon of meadows, woods and skies and with such a hospitable shade of alders and willows that it was in truth a retreat worthy of the pen of Virgil. Hidden and winding bypaths, the murmuring of many brooks, sweet and mossy banks, nothing was lacking in the surroundings.

141

It was really the mirror of a magician, that clear blue water that bubbled out from amid tiny pebbles and rose to reflect upon its bosom a scene so pastoral and picturesque.

There are places that make us think of the inhabitants of Eden before the fall and even make us think without rebuke of that sin itself now that we are no more inhabitants of Eden. Therefore, around that spring the gay young girls of Cordovado, of Venchieredo and even of Teglio, Fratta, Morsano, Cintello, Bagnarola and other villages around had been in the habit of gathering on festa evenings from time immemorial. And here they would remain for long, singing, talking, laughing, having picnics until their mothers, their lovers or the moon sent them home again. I do not need to tell you that with the girls there gathered also the young men; since that you could imagine for yourself. But what I want to point out is that when all accounts were closed at the year's end, I believe and affirm that more came to the spring of Venchieredo to make love than to drink their fill; and moreover that more wine than water was drunk there. Naturally, in such cases one must rather obey the compulsion of the ham and sausages than the superstition of running water.

I myself was many times at this enchanting spring, but once, and once only, did I dare to profane with my hand the virgin crystal of its surface. Hunting had brought me thither, broken with fatigue and burning with thirst; and moreover my flask of white wine had refused to shed any more tears for me. If I were to return there now perhaps I would drink deep draughts in order to make myself young again; but the hydropathic taste of old age would not make me forget the joyous and turbulent mouthfuls of good wine of former times.

As it happened, some years before me Leopardo Provedoni had acquired a familiarity with the spring of Venchieredo. This solitary, calm, remote spot suited his mood as a well-made suit fits the person. Every thought of his found there its natural corollary; or at least none of the willows intervened to say no to whatever he was thinking. He embellished, coloured and peopled in his own way the deserted landscape; and so,

142

without being as yet at war with anyone in the world, he still felt himself different from others and it seemed to him that there he lived more happily than elsewhere for the simple reason that there he was free and alone. This feeling which Leopardo had for the spring of Venchieredo was the first 'fact' of which he would not admit contradiction; the second was the love he bore, even more than for the spring, for a beautiful girl who often went there and whom he met alone there one lovely May morning. To hear him tell of this scene seemed to me like listening to a reading from the *Aminta*, but Tasso wrote his verses first and read them over afterwards; Leopardo remembered and, in remembering, improvised, so that to see and hear him was to feel on one's brow the cool dews of poetry.

He had left his house one fine sunny May day with his gun over his shoulder more to satisfy the curiosity of the passers-by than with any hostile intent towards the snipe and partridges. Step by step, with his head in the clouds, he found himself at the edge of the wood that surrounded the spring on two sides, and strained his ears for the usual salutation of a nightingale. The nightingale had indeed awaited his arrival and trilled its usual song, but not from the usual tree; that day the sound came, timid and subdued, from a more hidden branch and it seemed that his greeting was a little diffident because of the weapon his friend was carrying on his shoulder. Leopardo listened among the branches to spy out the new refuge of his harmonious host but, turning here and there, his glances suddenly succeeded in finding even more than they sought.

Oh, why was it not I who was enamoured of Doretta? Old as I am, I could write a page to bewilder my readers and take by assault the highest seats of poesy! I would that youth could mark the outlines, the heart lay on the colours and that youth and heart together could shine through every part of the picture with such magic that the good for tenderness and the bad for envy should take up the book again. Poor Leopardo! You alone could do much, you who for all your life carried painted in your eyes and graven upon your heart that spectacle of love.

143

And even now the uncertain memory of your words shines through me to thoughts so amorous and innocent that I cannot without tears trace these lines.

He sought, therefore, the nightingale and saw instead, seated on the bank of the stream that bubbled out of the spring, a young girl, who was dangling one foot in the water and with the other, bare and white as ivory, was tracing circles and curves among the little fish that darted on its surface. She smiled and clapped her hands from time to time when she succeeded in touching one of them with her foot and tossing it out of the water. Then the scarf which floated disordered on her breast opened to reveal the whiteness of her shoulders, half uncovered, and her cheeks flushed with pleasure without losing the radiance of innocence. The little fish did not cease their play except to return again after a brief fright, for in her hands she held the secret of this familiarity. A moment later she dipped her little foot in again very gently and having taken from under her apron a small piece of bread, she began to crumble it into pieces for her playmates. Then there was a coming and going, a rushing and darting, a competing and robbing of one another in this little family of living silver; and the young girl bent over them as if to receive their thanks. And then when the feast was at its height, she stirred the water with her feet, amused at their greed, which although they were terrified for the moment, soon made them recover their daring so as not to lose the choicest mouthfuls. This shuffling of her little feet showed a glimpse of the delicate shape of a rounded and well-formed leg; and the ends of her scarf became quite disordered on her shoulders and her breast seemed scarcely to be confined by her linen bodice, so much did merriment swell and agitate it.

Leopardo, at first all ears to listen to the nightingale, was now all eyes, without even being aware of the metamorphosis. This innocent girl, simple and gay, this joyous ignorance and unself-consciousness, this still girlish immodesty which recalled the nakedness of the cherubs that sported in Pordenone's pictures, the thousand charms of a slim and delicate figure,

144

eric fraser

that hair, golden-chestnut, curling over her temples like a boy's, that fresh and candid smile, made as if specially to enhance two rows of shining teeth as small and even as the beads of a crystal rosary; all these things, I say, were depicted with the colours of wonder in the young man's eyes. He would have given anything demanded of him to be one of those little fish, so familiar with her; he would have been content to remain there all his life only to watch her. But he was somewhat delicate in conscience, and these pleasures enjoyed by stealth, even in the rapture of ecstasy, filled him with a sort of remorse. He therefore began to whistle some tune or other, with what correctness you can well imagine, who know by experience the effect produced on the voice and lips by the first stimulus of love. Whistling tonelessly and tunelessly and bending back the branches that were in his way, he arrived, reeling like a drunken man, at the edge of the spring. The young girl arranged the kerchief on her shoulders but had no time to take her feet out of the water and so remained a little bashful and a little astonished at this unexpected visit.

Leopardo was a handsome youth; of that beauty that is made up of comeliness of form combined with strength and composure, the greatest attraction to the eye and which best reflects the ideal of divine perfection. He had something child-like in his expression, something of the philosopher in his brow and of the athlete in his figure; but his modest way of dressing in the peasant fashion greatly diminished the impression of this aspect. Therefore at first the girl was not so embarrassed as if it had been a gentleman who had thus appeared, and she became more reassured on raising her eyes to his face and recognizing him. She murmured in a voice almost of satisfaction: 'Ah, so it is the Signor Leopardo!'

The young man heard this quiet exclamation and for the first time his name seemed to him not sufficiently gracious and delicate to rest worthily on such lovely lips. But it overjoyed him to be already known to the girl and thus find himself freed from the necessity of having to introduce himself.

'And who are you, beautiful one?' he asked, stammering and

looking at the reflection in the water, since he had not yet courage enough to look at the original.

'I am Doretta, the daughter of the Chancellor of Venchieredo,' replied the girl.

'Ah, so you are the Signora Doretta!' exclaimed Leopardo, who despite his doubled desire to look at her, found himself greatly hindered by his confusion at having first treated her with so little respect.

The girl looked up as if meaning: 'Yes, it is most certainly I, and I do not see why you should be so surprised.' Leopardo gathered together all his reserves of courage to return to the charge, but he was so much a novice in the art of questioning that it was not strange that, on this first occasion, he cut a very mediocre figure.

'Don't you think it is very hot to-day?' he ventured.

'Enough to kill one,' replied Doretta.

'Do you think it will continue?' asked the other.

'That depends on your almanack,' said the girl maliciously, 'Schieson says yes and Strolich promises no.'

'And you, what do you think?' went on Leopardo, going from bad to worse.

'It is all one to me,' replied the girl, who was beginning to be amused at this dialogue. 'The Rector of Venchieredo calls for three-day rogations equally for drought or frost, and as far as I am concerned, praying for either one or the other does not make the slightest difference.'

'How lively and pleasant she is,' thought Leopardo; and this thought relieved his mind from that trying interrogation that had succeeded so well up till then.

'Have you had good hunting?' Doretta decided to ask, seeing him fall silent and not wanting to forgo so exquisite a chance to amuse herself.

'Oh!' exclaimed the young man, as if he had only just become aware of the gun slung over his shoulder.

'I bet you have forgotten the flint at home,' she went on, teasing him, 'or perhaps it is some new kind of gun?'

Leopardo's arquebus dated back to the first generation of

146

firearms and it was enough to look at it to realize all the malice of that pretended ingenuousness.

'It is a family heirloom,' the young man replied seriously, since he had thought on this subject often enough and knew its birth, life and miracles by family tradition. 'It fought in the Morea with my great-great-great-grandfather; my grandfather once killed with this very weapon twenty-two snipe in a single day, a thing that till then would have been thought impossible when one considers that it needs ten full minutes to load it and that after the firing of the powder in the touch-hole it needs another good half-minute before the discharge. However, my father has never succeeded in hitting more than ten, and up to the present, I have never exceeded six. But the snipe have begun to learn cunning and in that half-minute that it takes to fire, they have already flown half a mile away. The time will come when I have to run after them with the ramrod. However, I do the best I can with this old musket; but the trouble is that the catch no longer holds firm and at times I take aim and pull the trigger but after half a minute, when the explosion should take place, I find instead that the flint has fallen out. Then I must take it to Fratta, to Mastro Germano, to be mended. It is true that I could ask papa to get a new one, but I am sure that he would reply that I should not try to introduce novelties into the family. Indeed, that is also my own view. If the musket is a little out of sorts, after having gone through the Morea campaign and having killed twenty-two snipe in one day, one must really sympathize with it. None the less, as I say, I will take it to Mastro Germano to be repaired. Don't you think I am right, Signora Doretta?'

'Yes, certainly,' replied the girl, withdrawing her feet from the stream and wiping them on the grass, 'the snipe at least will say that you are right a thousand times.'

Leopardo meanwhile looked lovingly at the musket and polished its barrel with the sleeve of his jacket.

'For the moment we will repair it so,' he went on, taking a handful of flints out of his pocket and choosing the sharpest of them to put in the catch. 'You see, Signora Doretta, how I prepare for the unforeseen? I must always carry with me a bag full of flints, but it is not the fault of the musket if old age has blunted its teeth. One has to carry a powder-horn and a ram-rod and bullets, anyway; one can very well carry some flints too.'

'Surely. You are strong and that should not worry you,' added Doretta.

'You think so? For four little flints? I don't even feel I am carrying them,' replied the youth, putting them back in his pocket. 'I could even carry you as well as far as Venchieredo and would no more be out of breath than the barrel of my musket. I have good legs, excellent lungs and can walk to and from the Lugugnana marshes in a single morning.'

'*Caspita*, what a rush!' exclaimed the girl. 'When the Signor Count goes down there to hunt he goes only on horseback and stays away three days.'

'But I am quicker; I go and come back in a flash.'

'But without shooting anything?'

'How, without shooting anything? The ducks, fortunately, have not yet learnt the cunning of the snipe, and would await the convenience of my gun not for half a minute but for half an hour; I never come back from there save with a full bag. It is true that I go to hunt the game where it lives and am not afraid of plunging into the marshes up to my waist.'

'Mercy!' cried Doretta, 'aren't you afraid of getting drowned there?'

'I am only afraid of ills that have actually taken place,' replied Leopardo, 'and even to those I do not pay much atten-tion. I don't even think of the others and, since up to now I am not dead, I would not have the slightest fear of dying even though I found myself facing a whole file of muskets! It would be a fine thing to be afraid of an ill that one doesn't even know!'

Doretta, who up till then had been jesting at the simplicity of this youth, now began to look at him with a certain respect. Furthermore, Leopardo, now that he had surmounted the first obstacle, felt quite ready to open his heart, perhaps for the

148

first time, and the confessions that rose spontaneously and sincerely to his lips aroused his own curiosity as much as that of the girl. He had never before troubled to make a judgement on himself; and therefore listened to his own words as so many interesting novelties.

'Tell me the truth,' he went on, sitting down opposite the girl, who stopped glancing here and there for her sandals, 'tell me the truth; who taught you to love the spring of Venchieredo so well?'

The question distressed Doretta a little and it was her turn to be embarrassed. Chattering and joking she was expert enough in, perhaps more than was needful, but she was unable to give an account of anything without the greatest effort of gravity and concentration. None the less, strangely enough, when confronted with that good fellow, Leopardo, she could not succeed in turning the question aside with a joke and had to reply, stammering, that the nearness of the spring to her father's property had accustomed her from girlhood to play there and that, the habit once formed, she had gone on doing so.

'Very good,' replied Leopardo, who was too simple to have noticed her embarrassment as he had been too good-hearted to have noticed her earlier mockery, 'but aren't you afraid to play tricks with the waters of the brook?'

'Afraid?' said the girl, blushing, 'why should I be?'

'Because if you slipped in you might drown yourself.'

'I never even thought of such danger,' said Doretta.

'Nor do I think of it or of any others,' replied the young man, fixing his large tranquil blue eyes on the little sparkling ones of the girl. 'The world simply goes on with me and could very well go on without me. That is my comfort, and for the rest the good Lord will provide. But you, do you often come here to the spring?'

'Oh, very often,' replied Doretta, 'especially when it is hot.'

Leopardo thought that, as they had met just then, they could meet again many more times; but such a thought seemed to him too daring and he confined himself to a long look of hope and longing. However, with his lips he began talking of

149

the heat and the time of year and said that, for him, winter and spring were all one. He would not even notice the difference save for the leaves turning brown and falling.

'I love the spring best of all!' put in Doretta.

'I also,' exclaimed Leopardo.

'But surely . . . are they not all the same to you?' said the girl.

'That's true. It seems to me . . . but . . . to-day is such a lovely day that it makes me give the palm to this season of the year above all. I meant, when I said they were all one to me, only as regards the heat and the cold. As regards the pleasure of the eyes, I am sure that the spring comes first of all!'

'And yet that scoundrel of a Gaetano at Venchieredo always defends the winter,' went on the girl.

'That Gaetano is really a scoundrel,' replied the other.

'Oh, so you know him too?' asked Doretta.

'Yes . . . that is . . . isn't he the gatekeeper?' stammered Leopardo. 'I have a vague idea that I have heard his name.'

'No, he is not the gatekeeper, he is the Serjeant,' said the girl, 'with him it is always a question of going to extremes over a trifle. I never want to hear winter spoken of, and he always praises it to the skies just to spite me.'

'Oh, I'll make him hold his tongue,' exclaimed Leopardo.

'You will? . . . Then you must come some time or another,' replied Doretta, rising to her feet and putting on her sandals. 'But be sure and bring a good dose of patience with you, for that Gaetano is as stubborn as a donkey.'

'I'll come all right,' said Leopardo, 'but I shall see you again at the spring, shan't I?'

'Yes, certainly; when the whim takes me,' replied the girl, 'and on festas I am always here with the other girls of the district.'

'On festas, on festas,' murmured the young man.

'Oh, you must come,' broke in the girl, 'and you will see what a paradise we have here all around.'

Leopardo followed Doretta, who was returning to Venchieredo, like a dog that follows its master after having been chased away. Doretta turned around from time to time to look at him

150

smilingly; he too smiled but his heart was pounding so heavily that it made him tremble. So at last they reached the gateway to the village.

'Good-bye, Signor Leopardo!' the girl cried to him from a distance.

'Good-bye, Signora Doretta,' replied the young man with a look so intent and prolonged that it seemed he would send his soul with it, and bent, blushing, to pick up some flowers that she had mischievously dropped. Then, when the leafy pergola of the vines had hidden from his sight the slim graceful form of Doretta, who was hurrying towards the castle, his look fell to the ground so gravely, so seriously, that it seemed as if seeking eternal burial there. Some moments later he looked up with a sigh and went his way homewards with his head filled, if not with new thoughts, certainly with very new and strange ideas. Those few little flowers he put next his heart and kept them for ever after.

Leopardo had fallen in love with the girl; that was all. But how and why had he fallen in love? The how was certainly by looking at her and listening to her; the why nobody will ever know; as one can never know why sky blue appeals to one, scarlet to others and orange to others still. Girls as pretty as Doretta, or even three times prettier, he had seen at Cordovado, at Fossalta and at Portogruaro, and indeed the daughter of the Chancellor of Venchieredo was too slim for real perfection; yet he had never shown any interest in these, though he had had every chance of being with them and talking with them, but on the other hand was well cooked at the first sight of this one.

Perhaps familiarity takes away from rather than adds to the force of feminine charm? I do not say so; it would be too unfair to women. Among them there are many who do not impress at first glance but who, when familiar by long habit, gradually warm the heart until at last they create a conflagration that may not be extinguished. There are others who consume us in their flame at the mere sight, but often of the flame thus kindled there soon remains only ashes. But as there are men of

151

straw who, even slowly warmed, end in nothing, so also there can be found hearts of iron which become red-hot in a moment and do not cool again. Love is a universal law, which has as many various corollaries as have the souls subject to it. To dictate a complete and practical treatise on it, one would need to create a library wherein every man and woman should deposit a volume of their own observations. One would read therein the noblest and the vilest things, the most celestial and the most bestial that the imagination of a novelist might conceive. But the difficulty would be that such writings should obey the first impulse of sincerity; since many enter into love with preconceived ideas, and desire according to them and not according to the force of their sentiments. Thence comes the abuse of those terrible words 'for ever' which are often spoken so light-heartedly in conversations and lovers' vows.

Doretta of Venchieredo certainly did not seem created to satisfy the grave, warm-hearted and concentrated spirit of Leopardo. None the less, she was the first who commanded his heart to live and to live completely and for ever in her. Another mystery, no less obscure and sorrowful than the others, since the one who might have satisfied him better did not move in his spirit any of those desires that compose or lead to love. Would it be, perhaps, so ordained in the mortal scheme that like avoids like, while opposites search each other out? But not even this could I affirm in the face of so many examples that contradict it. One can only suspect that if material things wandering confusedly in space have been subjected for centuries to a regulating force, so the spiritual and inner world still perhaps awaits in a state of chaos that virtue that co-ordinates it.

Meanwhile it is a contrast of sentiments, of forces, of judgements; an unformed and tumultuous medley of passions, of nobility and of vileness, a real chaos of spirit not yet developed from matter, and of matter urging disorder upon the spirit. Everything is agitated, is moving, is changing; but, I once more repeat it, the kernel of this future order is already existent and every day gathers around itself new elements, as those

152

nebulae that in turning grow larger, grow denser or thinner in the atmosphere of atoms that surrounds them. How many centuries are necessary for this nebula to grow from an atom to a star? The astronomers will tell you. How many centuries does it need for human sentiment to crystallize into conscience? The anthropologists will tell you. But as the star matures, perhaps at the last and disordered ends of the universe, into another solar system, so conscience promises to the internal disorder of the sentiments a stable and truly moral harmony. There are spaces of time which are confounded with eternity in the thought of man; but what is denied to thought is not forbidden to hope. The spirit of man can hope for long and await with patience.

But even poor Leopardo, though he had not to look forward to a life of centuries, had to await with patience for Doretta first to show herself aware of his intentions and then to judge him acceptable to her. But, first of all, Leopardo was handsome, then he was one of the best matches in the district and finally he gave her so many proofs of a devoted love that it would have been sheer foolishness not to take advantage of them. Further, though he often amused her by his simplicity, he often also fascinated her by the outlook of his valiant and serene soul. She was aware that, though he was peaceable and tolerant with women even when they made game of him, he was by no means so with the young men around him. A glance from him was enough to make them fold their wings and it was no small glory for her to have always attentive to her nods one who so easily curbed the insistence of others.

Doretta therefore allowed herself to be found often enough at the spring and behaved even more kindly towards Leopardo at the festa gatherings; though from accepting his courtesies to returning them the road was long enough, yet one step after another, at last it came to an end. Then Leopardo no longer contented himself with seeing her on those mornings when she chanced to appear, or at the festas, among the throng, but went every evening to Venchieredo and there, either walking in the village or on the staircase of the Chancellery, would

153

remain with her until the hour for supper. Then he saluted her again, more with the heart than with the lips, and made his way back to Cordovado, whistling his accustomed tune with greater assurance.

So the two young people arranged their life between them. As to their elders, it was a different story. The most illustrious Dr. Natalino, Chancellor of Venchieredo, let matters take their course, since he had seen so many flies buzzing around his Doretta that one more or less did not disturb him in the least. Signor Antonio, however, as soon as he noticed the affair began to stick his nose in the air and to give a hundred other signs of ill-humour. He was of peasant stock and a peasant through and through and could not be pleased that his son should move in another sphere. He therefore began to put his nose in the air, a manoeuvre that left Leopardo quite unruffled; so seeing that was not enough, he adopted sterner measures, began to scold him and to speak to him with a certain gravity that seemed to say: 'I am not quite satisfied with you.' But Leopardo was very satisfied with himself and believed that he was giving an example of Christian patience in putting up with the ill-humour of his father. But when Signor Antonio came, as they say, to breaking the ice and speaking openly and explaining fairly and squarely the reasons for his upturned nose, then Leopardo also felt himself obliged to explain fairly and squarely in return his unshakable determination to continue on his present course.

'Aren't you ashamed of yourself, going sniffing after all those fine feathers? What will they think of it in the district? Haven't you seen that even the Venchieredo buli are laughing at you? And how do you think this fine game of yours is going to end? Aren't you afraid that some time or other the castellan will get his servants to throw you out? Perhaps you like putting me into bad odour with that gentleman, who you know is already pretty hard to please? . . .' With these and similar complaints the prudent Mayor went on attacking and striking at his Absalom, but Leopardo paid no attention to such nonsense, as he called it. He replied that he too was a man like any other and that if he loved Doretta it was certainly not a matter

154

to laugh at or to forgo at the banter of the first newcomer. Signor Antonio raised his voice, Leopardo shrugged his shoulders, and each stuck to his own views, and I believe too that these arguments still further excited the already inflamed spirits of the young man.

However, it soon became evident that the old man's misgivings might not have been misplaced. If Doretta always welcomed her suitor warmly, all the other inhabitants of Venchieredo did not show an equal complaisance. Amongst these was that Gaetano, who was captain of the castellan's buli and who perhaps himself boasted some pretensions to the young lady and could not stomach the thought of the handsome youth from Cordovado and his daily visits. They began with jests, advanced to arguments and at one time ended up by exchanging a few blows. But Leopardo was so calm, so deliberate, that the bulo had to slink away with his tail between his legs; and this defeat on the public square in no way helped to lessen his hostility.

It must be added that Doretta, more vainglorious for herself than enamoured of Leopardo, enjoyed the war that had broken out about her and certainly did nothing to calm it. Gaetano whispered so much in the ear of his patron about the arrogance of the young Provedoni and his lack of respect for persons of high rank and in particular for the Signor Magistrate, that to satisfy him, he ended by regarding Leopardo with an even more hostile eye than he did the majority of men. His attitude seemed to say 'Keep clear of my feet!' and it was well understood for ten good miles around that such a hostile look from the castellan of Venchieredo was equivalent to a sentence of banishment for at least two months.

Leopardo, however, was looked at, looked in his turn and went quietly on his way. Gaetano asked no more, for he knew very well that this tacit defiance would have counted for a hundred crimes in the opinion of his haughty castellan. Indeed the latter was very much irritated to see Leopardo take so little heed of his glances and after having encountered him two, three or four times in the courtyard of the castle, he once stopped him and said resentfully that Leopardo had too much time to waste and that all this walking from Cordovado to Venchieredo might give him a pain in the loins. Leopardo bowed and did not understand, or pretended not to understand, and went on walking as before without fear of endangering his health.

The Signor then began, as they say, to find Leopardo really getting on his nerves and seeing that he had accomplished nothing by half-measures, one afternoon had Leopardo summoned and told him clearly that he did not maintain his castle for the convenience of the young gentlemen of Cordovado and that, if he needed love, he should try his fortune with other girls, and not with those of Venchieredo, but that if he wanted a good beating he should come that evening to his usual tryst and he would be served as well as he could wish.

Leopardo bowed again but did not say a word; but the same evening he did not fail to go to Doretta who, be it said, was proud to see him defy such a storm for her sake and rewarded him with redoubled tenderness. Gaetano fumed, the castellan looked askance even at his dogs and all of them gave every indication that they were concocting some dirty trick among themselves. Indeed, one fine night (that very night on which I received a nocturnal visit from the Pisana after having returned to Fratta on the crupper of the unknown, bearded cavalier), when Leopardo had just taken leave of his adored one and was scrambling over the village fence to return to Cordovado, three villainous rogues leapt on him and began to set about him so vigorously that he, overcome by their sudden attack, was thrown to the ground and was in a bad way. But at that moment a wild dark figure leapt out of the hedge and commenced to batter the three ruffians with the butt of his musket and to set about them with such a will that it was their turn to defend themselves and Leopardo, having recovered from his first surprise, set about them in his turn.

'Dogs! I'll let you have it!' shouted the new arrival, rushing after the three bravos, who were flying towards the castle bridge.

But they, avoiding the blows of the two demons behind them,

156

ran so quickly that their assailants were unable to catch them up save at the very gates. Fortunately these were barred so that, however loudly they shouted for them to be opened, and opened at once, there was plenty of time to get in a few blows. Scarcely had the gatekeeper opened the wicket than they rushed inside as though escaping from the clutches of the devil.

'Ho, there! I know you!' one of them, Gaetano himself, said, turning round. 'You are the Spaccafumo and you'll pay dearly for your insolence and for daring to meddle in what doesn't concern you!'

'Yes, yes, I am the Spaccafumo,' shouted the one outside, 'and I'm not afraid of you or your ill-born patron or thousands like you.'

'Did you hear? Did you hear?' shouted Gaetano as he secured the gate with stout chains. 'As God lives, the patron will have him hanged!'

'Perhaps. But first I shall hang you!' shouted the Spaccafumo in reply, departing with Leopardo, who retreated unwillingly from that gate closed in his face.

The smuggler retired behind the hedge, mounted his horse and wanted to escort the young man back to Cordovado.

'How did you happen to arrive so opportunely?' Leopardo asked him, feeling more shame than pleasure at another's help in his own predicament.

'I got wind of what was going to happen and was waiting there on purpose,' replied the Spaccafumo.

'Rogues! Villains! Traitors!' cursed the young man.

'Quiet! That's their job,' said the Spaccafumo. 'Let us talk of other things. What do you think of me to-day as a horseman? You know that a short time ago I decided to give my legs a rest, since they are no longer as young as they were, and I thought the legs of the colts that pasture in the lagoons should take their turn. To-day the lot fell on this one and I have come here from down Lugugnana way in less than an hour and also gave a lift on my crupper as far as Fratta to a boy who had lost his way in the marshes.'

'But tell me how you came to know of the plot,' interrupted

157

Leopardo, who was still thinking over the dirty trick that had been played him.

'No, I am not going to tell you,' replied the Spaccafumo, 'and now that you are at your own door, I will say a cordial good night. We shall meet again soon.'

'But why? Won't you come in and sleep at our house?'

'No, no, the air there is not good for my lungs.'

As he said this, the Spaccafumo was already on his way and I could not tell you where he spent the night. Certainly at noon the next day he was seen to enter the house of the Chaplain of Fratta, who was his spiritual father and was said to receive him with great respect owing to the fear he had of him. But a little later there came to Fratta four assassins from Venchieredo who, having learnt that the Spaccafumo was with the Chaplain, went openly to the parsonage. They knocked and knocked again, called and called again, until at last the Chaplain, all drowsy and feigning ignorance of what they wanted, came to open the door and ask them their business.

'What do we want, indeed!' replied Gaetano furiously, rushing off towards the fields behind the parsonage where he could see a man on horseback at full gallop. 'That's who we want! Come on, come on, all of you! The Signor Chaplain will pay for his part in this later.'

The poor priest fell back in an armchair, fainting with fright, while the four buli began to run across the furrows, hoping that the thickets and ditches would cut down the speed of the fugitive. But the peasants were of the opinion that if the Spaccafumo had never allowed himself to be caught when he was on foot, it was even less likely that this misfortune should occur now that he was mounted. The Signori buli would merely have wasted their breath to no avail.

These matters were already known in the Castle of Fratta and were being discussed as grave and mysterious events, when we three, the Pisana, myself and the apothecary's son, returned. The Count and the Chancellor were running around looking for Marchetto and the Captain. Fulgenzio had flown to the bell-tower and was ringing the bells as if the hayloft were on fire; Monsignor Orlando, rubbing his eyes, was asking what had happened and the Countess busied herself in ordering the doors and windows to be barred and the fortress put in a state of defence. When God willed, the Captain managed to recruit three men who, with two muskets and a blunderbuss, were drawn up in the courtyard to await the orders of His Excellency. His Excellency ordered them to go to the piazza and see if public order had been disturbed and give their armed support to the authorities against all evil-doers and especially against the said Spaccafumo. Germano lowered the drawbridge with many grumbles and the valiant soldiers went out.

The Spaccafumo had, however, no intention to let himself be seen that day on the piazza of Fratta; and however much the Captain displayed his ugliest face and brushed up his moustaches at the door of the inn, nobody appeared who dared to defy so menacing a frown. This was a great satisfaction for the Captain, and when the Venchieredo buli returned towards evening from their useless chase, tired and panting like so many hounds, he did not fail to complain about them. Gaetano sneered at him to his face with scant show of politeness, so much so indeed that the three Fratta Cernide were panic-stricken and dived into the inn, abandoning their leader. But the Captain was a man of the sword and the toga; and did not find it hard to defend himself decorously against Gaetano's sneers. He pretended to be aware, only then, that the Spaccafumo had fled on horseback across the fields. To listen to him, one would have thought he was only waiting for the villain to emerge from his hiding-place at any moment and then would make him pay dearly for the affront shown to the authority of the noble magistrate of Venchieredo. Gaetano replied to these overbearing remarks that his patron was more than capable of exacting payment himself and that furthermore the Chaplain should be told that they would think over how to settle accounts with him for the night's shelter that he had given the Spaccafumo.

That afternoon nobody dreamed of going outside the castle; the Pisana and I spent a dull and irritating day squabbling in

159

the courtyard with the sons of Fulgenzio and the bailiff. And in the evening Germano, from his gate-room, questioned every visitor who arrived and only when he had received assurances from without, lowered the drawbridge so that they could enter. The rusty chains squealed on the pulleys as if in protest at having been set to work again after so many years of tranquil ease; and no one passed over the uneven planking without first glancing with little confidence at the cracks that opened beneath them.

Lucilio and the Partistagno remained that evening in the castle later than usual; but their laughter was hardly enough to calm the nerves of the Countess who saw the whole jurisdiction of Fratta already in flames as a result of this enmity between the Spaccafumo and the Count of Venchieredo.

The next day, which was Sunday, there was fresh news in the countryside. At half past seven, when the people were returning from the first Mass at Teglio, a great clattering of horses' hooves was heard and a little later the Lord of Venchieredo with three of his buli appeared in the market-place. He was a man of middle age, florid and sturdy, in whose eyes one could not say whether cunning or ferocity was the more evident, but proud and arrogant above all others, as could be judged from his voice and bearing. He drew up his horse abruptly and asked harshly which was the house of the Most Reverend Chaplain of Fratta. The parsonage was pointed out to him and he entered there with the air of a master, after handing his reins to Gaetano, who had accompanied him.

The Chaplain had only just been shaved and was at that moment under the orders of the servant-girl who was finishing his tonsure. Their laboratory was the kitchen and the little priest, who had somewhat recovered from his fright of the day before, was joking with Giustina, telling her to cut his crown properly and not as at the last festa when the whole church had burst out laughing as soon as he had lifted his biretta. Giustina for her part was studying her problem so intently that she had no time to reply to these sallies; but, shorn here and shaven there, the tonsure grew larger, like a splash of oil on the poor

160

priest's head, and though he had given her orders not to make it larger than a half-ducat there was already no coin in existence big enough to cover it.

'Ah, Giustina, Giustina,' sighed the Chaplain, feeling the extent of his new tonsure with his hand, 'it seems that we have gone a little too close to this ear.'

'No doubt about it,' replied Giustina, who was a good-natured and clumsy peasant woman in her thirties, though she looked about forty-five, 'but if we are too near this ear we shall have to go a little further from that.'

'*Cospetto!* Do you want to pluck me like a friar?' exclaimed the patient.

'No, no, I have never plucked you,' said the woman, 'and I won't pluck you to-day, either.'

'No, no, I tell you . . . let it alone . . . enough!'

'On the contrary . . . let me finish . . . keep still and don't move for a moment. . . .'

'Eh, you women are the devil!' murmured the Chaplain. 'If it were a question of fashion, you would even allow yourselves to be tonsured . . .'

Who knows what he might have added to the word 'tonsured' if he had not stopped, hearing a noise at the door like the rattling of spurs. He leapt to his feet, pushed Giustina aside, snatched the towel from around his neck and, turning round, found himself face to face with the Lord of Venchieredo. What a grimace, what eyes, what an appearance the poor priest then made may be left to the imagination! He remained in that uncertain attitude of wonder, of fear, of curiosity in which he had first become aware of the menacing appearance of the castellan. His mantle fell to the ground and between the folds of his doublet he moved his hands weakly as if to say: 'Now we are in the soup!'

'Oh, most beloved Chaplain, how is your health?' the feudatory began.

'Well . . . I really don't know . . . that is . . . take a seat . . . the pleasure is mine . . .' stammered the priest.

'It doesn't seem to be so great a pleasure,' went on the

161

castellan. 'You have the most terror-stricken expression, Your Reverence. Oh perhaps,' he went on, turning a mocking eye on Giustina, 'I have interrupted some canonical labour?'

'Oh no, no,' murmured the Chaplain, 'I was . . . Giustina, put on water for coffee or chocolate. Would you like chocolate, Signor Count . . . Your Excellency?'

'Go and feed the hens. I want to talk to His Reverence alone,' replied the castellan, turning to Giustina.

She did not wait to be told twice and wriggled her way into the courtyard, still holding the razor in her hand. The castellan then addressed the Chaplain and, taking him by the arm, drew him towards the fireplace where, before he knew what was happening, the priest found himself seated on a bench.

'Now to our affairs,' said the castellan, seating himself opposite. 'A fire freshly kindled does not spoil the skin even in summer, they say. But tell me truthfully, Your Reverence, are you a priest or a smuggler?'

The poor wretch quivered all over and made so many grimaces that, however often he resettled his collar or twisted his lips, he was unable to resume his normal expression for the whole of the subsequent conversation.

'They are both occupations and I don't want to make any comparisons,' went on the Count, 'I am only asking for my own information which you intend to exercise. For priests, there are alms, capons and tithes; for smugglers, musket-shots, prison and the noose. Everyone is free to choose; and in such a case I do not say that I would choose the priest. Only it seems to me that the canons should forbid a mingling of these two professions. What do you say, Your Reverence?'

'Yes, Signor, Your Excellency . . . I am quite of your opinion,' stammered the priest.

'Well then, reply,' said the Venchieredo. 'Are you a priest or a smuggler?'

'Your Excellency . . . is joking.'

'Joking! I? Oh no, Your Reverence! . . . I got up at dawn, and when I do that I am in no mood for joking! . . . I have come to tell you, fairly and squarely, that if the Signor Count

162

of Fratta is not able to safeguard the interests of the Most Serene Republic, I am not far away and feel myself quite capable of doing so. You receive in your house smugglers and contraband. No, no, Your Reverence, it is no good shaking your head . . . we have witnesses and at need could bring them forward in perfect accord with the Courts. . . .'

'Mercy!' exclaimed the Chaplain.

'However,' continued the feudatory, 'since it is in no way pleasant to me to have such bands as neighbours, I will ask you to take a change of air at your discretion, before I am compelled to make you change it by force.'

'A change of air? What do you mean? To change air, me? How? Please explain, Your Excellency!'

'I mean to say that if you could obtain a parish in the mountains you would be showing real finesse.'

'In the mountains?' said the Chaplain, even more astounded. 'I, in the mountains? It is impossible, Your Excellency. Why, I don't even know where the mountains are.'

'They are there,' remarked the castellan, with a gesture towards the window.

But the castellan had reckoned without the excessive timidity of the priest. In certain beings, rough, simple, modest but individual and primitive timidity may sometimes take the place of courage; and to the Chaplain the necessity of commencing a new life in a new country, with people unknown to him, seemed a burden even heavier and more formidable than to die. He had been born in Fratta, had his roots there and felt that if he were uprooted from this place he would never survive it.

'No, Your Excellency,' he replied, with more assurance than he had shown hitherto, 'I must die at Fratta, as I have lived; and as for the mountains, if I were to be sent there, I doubt if I should reach them alive.'

'Very well then,' said the petty tyrant, rising, 'you will reach them dead, then; but in one way or another, I assure you that the accomplice of Spaccafumo will not remain Chaplain of Fratta. Bear that well in mind.'

163

Saying this, the nobleman gave a great rattling of spurs on the step of the hearth and went out of the parsonage followed by the priest with hanging head. The latter made one last bow as he saw the Count mount and then returned to talk things over with Giustina, who had been listening to the whole conversation from behind the courtyard door.

'Oh no, no, they must not bundle you off to the mountains!' whimpered the woman. 'Surely some evil would overtake you if you went so far! . . . and then, aren't your own people here? . . . What should we say to the Good Lord when He decided to take account of us?'

'Put that razor away, my daughter,' replied the priest. 'You can be quite sure that I shall not go to the mountains! . . . They can put me in the stocks, but in another parish, no, certainly not! . . . Can you imagine me at the tender age of forty finding myself among new faces and having to begin again from the beginning all that drudgery which I have gone through since childhood? No, Giustina! . . . I have said it and I repeat it: I will die in Fratta. But for all that it is a heavy cross that now weighs upon my neck; but I must bear it in holy peace. Ufff! . . . that Signor Magistrate! What an ugly snout he showed me! . . . But rather than move, I can put up with anything; and if he should play me some other dirty trick, what can I do about it? Better to be at odds with his buli than with someone else's. . . . At least I know them and will mind less being beaten by them.'

'But what are you saying?' said the servant. 'Even the buli should be submissive to you. How does it seem to you that a priest should be like the head of a nail to be driven here and there?'

'Little more, little more, my daughter, in these days. We must be patient!'

At this the sacristan entered to warn him that the people were waiting for him to say Mass; and the poor man, recollecting that he was already late, rushed out to fulfil his duties with his tonsure only half finished. In vain Giustina ran after him with the razor in her hand as far as the piazza; and the

164

ragged tonsure of the Chaplain and the sight of the Signor of Venchieredo, added to the events of the previous day, gave rise to the most singular comments.

The next day an imposing letter from the Lord of Venchieredo arrived for the Count of Fratta in which, without beating about the bush, he prayed his illustrious colleague to evict the Chaplain in the shortest possible time, accusing him of a thousand villainies, including that of assisting to defraud the Customs of the Most Serene Republic and of being an accomplice of the most desperate smugglers of the lagoons. 'And since such a crime must be hateful to the Most Excellent Signoria,' so ran the letter, 'how great is the merit of whoever hastens to punish it and how capital the danger to those ill-advised persons who for private reasons leave it unpunished, you, Most Illustrious Signor Magistrate, must know as well as any. The statutes and the proclamations speak clearly; and one's head may well be in question since monies are the life-blood of the state and he who by his negligence conspires to drain it of this truly vital fluid is guilty of a crime against the state.' As can be seen, the castellan had found the right road, and the Count of Fratta, on hearing this antiphonal read to him by the Chancellor, wriggled so much on his armchair that his customary majesty was much impaired. He had hoped to keep the facts of the matter secret; but the summoning of the Chaplain, the visit received by him the previous morning, his bewilderment, his gossiping with Giustina had all revealed to the entire countryside what had happened and had resulted in an uproar.

The Chaplain was loved by all as a good spiritual father; and further, the people of Fratta, accustomed to the patriarchal Venetian type of government by its magistrates, had the trait of not liking to allow anyone to put a foot upon their necks. There was much murmuring against the insolence of the castellan of Venchieredo and to the dismay of the Signor Count, the very inmates of the castle, by their stubborn and imprudent bearing, showed that they too wanted to bring down this ugly storm upon his head.

I had never seen the Count and his Chancellor so indivisible

165

as in those days; they resembled two weather-beaten rafters which leant one upon the other in order to stand up against a high wind; if one moved, the other immediately felt that he was falling and followed the movements of the first so as to keep in balance. Many arguments were put forward to curb the dangerous agitation of spirits, but the remedies were usually worse than the disease. They bit with greater gusto into the forbidden fruit; and tongues, bridled in the kitchen, broke out the more violently in the piazza or at the inn.

More than anyone else, Mastro Germano stormed against the arrogance of his former master. By the virulence of his philippics and the daring with which he defended the Chaplain, he became practically the ringleader of the disorder. Every evening, seated on an alehouse bench, he held forth in a loud voice on the necessity of not allowing this sole representative of the poor, their village priest, to be taken from them. Let the arrogant ones stir up trouble, he said, but there was justice for all and certain past sins might come to light which would send the judges to prison and leave the accused triumphant. Fulgenzio, the sacristan, navigated wisely through all this confusion; and although he had within the castle an official position of trust, outside it he never wearied of trying to pry out of Germano with every circumspection what truth there might be in these menacing hints.

One evening, when the gatekeeper had drunk more than he should have, Fulgenzio pestered him to such an extent that he quite let down his guard and sang and shouted to the four winds that the Signor castellan of Venchieredo would have had him put out of the way, had not he, poor brushwielder, been in a position to publish certain old tales that would have given the noble lord a very bad Eastertide.

Fulgenzio asked for no more. He did his best to change the subject and tried to show that the words of the old toper were either of no importance or the ravings of a drunkard. He then returned to his home to say the Rosary with his wife and children. But the next day, being market-day in Portogruaro, he went there early in the morning and returned even later

166

than usual. He was seen, when there, to enter the house of the Vice-captain of Justice, but being, as I have said, a sort of un-official writer to the Chancellery, the fact aroused no particular comment. But a week later, just as the case for sending the Chaplain to breathe the air of the mountains was about to come before the Courts, the Chancellery of Fratta received from Venice a formal order to desist from all further action in the matter and to institute instead an inquisitorial and secret in-vestigation on the person of Mastro Germano concerning revelations of great importance to the Signoria which he could and must make regarding the past life of the Most Illustrious Magistrate of Venchieredo.

A meteorite fallen from the moon to interrupt the revels of a band of bon-viveurs could not have caused greater astonish-ment and consternation than that decree. The Count and the Chancellor completely lost their heads and felt ready to sink into the earth; and since in their first bewilderment, they had failed to take shelter behind their usual reserve, the fears of the Countess and of Monsignor and the joy of the rest of the family showed itself in a thousand ways at the news and made their state of mind still more deplorable.

The position was indeed critical; on the one side was the im-minent and proved insolence of a feudatory accustomed to scorn every law, human and divine; on the other the imperious, inexorable, secret tribunals of the Venetian Inquisition. Here the perils of a ferocious vendetta, there the terrifying spectre of a punishment, secret, terrible and inevitable. On the right hand, a fearful vision of buli armed to the teeth, of blunder-busses ambushed behind hedges; on the left, the sinister appari-tion of Messer Grande, of deep dungeons, glowing irons, nooses, pincers and axes. The two illustrious magistrates felt their heads swimming for forty-eight hours; but, as was to be fore-seen, in the end they decided to offer the cake to the largest dog, since to reconcile the two of them was an enterprise not even to be attempted.

I cannot, however, conceal that the encouragements of the Partistagno and the wise counsels of Lucilio Vianello helped considerably to tip the balance to this side; and the Signor Count felt a little more secure at finding himself flanked by persons so valorous and so wise. This, however, in no way altered that the investigation of Germano remained wrapped in the most impenetrable shades of mystery; but those shades were not so impenetrable as to prevent prying eyes wanting to see beyond at all costs. Indeed, there was so much whispering that the old bulo of Venchieredo, terror-stricken by the decree of the inquisitors, had produced as evidence against his former master certain writings of ancient date, which strongly reflected upon his fidelity to the government of the Most Serene Republic, and that if on these hypotheses (let it be well understood that they were no more than hypotheses, because after the interrogation had been opened, the Count, the Chancellor and Mastro Germano, who alone were taking part in it, had become like deaf-mutes), if on these hypotheses, I say, some very fanciful structures were built, I leave it to you to imagine.

As might well be believed, one of the first to get wind of what was happening was the castellan of Venchieredo himself and it was obvious that he did not feel his conscience entirely clear, since at first he showed that he was more worried about the affair than he later wished to admit. He thought, observed, weighed and thought again and finally, one fine day, when they had just risen from the table at Fratta, his visit was announced to the Signor Count.

The Chaplain, who was in the kitchen, believed that at the announcement of that name he would faint then and there; as for the Signor Count, after having sought counsel from the eyes of those at table with him, no less amazed and uncertain than his own, he told the servant, stammering, to show the visitor into the room above and to say that he and the Chancellor would come up immediately. There were too many menaces, risks and dangers connected with this visit to be able to hope for any preliminary discussion, and, furthermore, the two worthies were not such eagles as to finish such a deliberation in a couple of minutes. Therefore they put their heads into the sack with resignation and went upstairs to meet the dreaded

168

arrogance and the no less dreaded cunning of the haughty castellan. The family remained in the dining-hall with their hearts beating as must those of the family of Regulus when the question was being debated in the Senate whether he should be kept in Rome or sent back to Carthage.

'Your Lordship's servant!' began Venchieredo quickly, as soon as the Count and his shadow set foot in the room. And he turned on that shadow a glance that made him three times more livid and obscure than before.

'Your Excellency's most humble servant!' replied the Count, without raising his eyes from the floor where he seemed to be seeking an inspiration to get him out of this encounter. But since no inspiration came, he turned to ask counsel of the Chancellor and felt most uneasy at seeing that he had withdrawn to the far wall. 'Signor Chancellor . . .' he managed to mutter.

But the Venchieredo cut his words short.

'It is useless,' he said, 'it is useless for the Signor Chancellor to be kept from his usual duties to waste time listening to our chatter. It is well known that he has in hand many most important cases which require careful treatment and the most diligent examination. The good of the Most Serene Signoria must come first! Is it not so, Signor Chancellor? Moreover you can safely leave us here together since our conversation is in no way concerned with legal matters and we can settle everything between ourselves.'

The Chancellor could hardly find the strength necessary to drag his feet out of the room, and his squint was at that moment so marked that he hit his nose against the jamb of the door. The Count made towards him a silent and impotent gesture of fear, entreaty and desperation, such a gesture as the arms of a drowning man, gasping for air, might make before he abandoned himself to the stream. Then, when the door had closed, he settled his lace waistcoat and lifted his eyes timidly, as if to say: 'Let us conduct ourselves with dignity!'

'I am pleased that you have received me with so much confidence,' declared the Venchieredo, 'that shows that we shall end by coming to an understanding. After all, you have done rightly, since I must discuss with you a most confidential matter. We shall come to an understanding, Signor Count, shall we not?' added the old fox, coming close to the other to shake his hand craftily.

The Signor Count was somewhat relieved by this sign of friendliness; he let his hand be shaken with a slight hesitation and felt a sense of constraint until he had concealed it hastily in a pocket of his cloak. I believe he chose the first possible moment to go and wash it, lest the Vice-captain of Porto-gruaro might sense upon it the odour of that greeting.

'Yes, Signor,' he replied, summoning up a little smile, an effort which brought tears to his eyes. 'Yes, Signor, I believe . . . that is . . . we have always been in agreement!'

'Well said, by God!' said the other, sitting down beside him in an armchair. 'We have always been in agreement and we shall be in complete agreement this time also. The nobility, however varied in customs, temperament and affinities, have none the less common interests. A wrong done to one of its members affects all the others. So it is necessary to stand firmly united and support one another and to assist whenever possible to maintain our privileges inviolate. Justice is good, indeed very good . . . for those who have need of it. For my part I feel that I have all the justice I need in my own house and those who try to use it against me cause me a great deal of trouble. Is it not true, Signor Count, that for you too all these pretensions by certain persons who want to meddle in our affairs are by no means pleasant?'

'Eh? . . . Just so . . . that is quite clear . . .' stammered the Count, who had also sat down automatically and of all those words had heard no more than a confused murmur and a sort of droning like a machine turning in his ear.

'And more,' went on the Venchieredo, 'the justice of such persons is not always the most expeditious or the best served; whoever wishes to obey it like a child can easily find himself at loggerheads with those who hold different views and have at their command another justice, rapid and effective.'

These phrases, pronounced one by one and, so to speak, underlined by the firm and curt accents of the speaker, deeply shocked the Count and made him raise a face I know not whether more scandalized or terrified as he grasped their meaning. But since to show indignation might expose him to some unpleasant explanations, he was sufficiently diplomatic to have recourse a second time to his usual smile, which this time obeyed his summons rather more tardily than the first.

'I see that you have understood me,' the other went on, 'and that you are able to weigh the force of my arguments, and that the favour I have come to ask of you will seem neither strange nor excessive.'

The Count opened his eyes very wide and took his hand out of his pocket to place it on his heart.

'Some evil tongue, some slanderous and lying scoundrel whom I will punish with a whipping, have no doubt about that,' continued the Venchieredo, 'has done me the favour of putting me in bad odour with the Signoria for I know not what trifles of long ago which are not even worth recalling. These are mere stupidities, mere fatuousness, everyone agrees; but in Venice they have to take account of these matters so as not to do wrong to their code. Your Excellency understands me; if they pass over frivolous denunciations in silence, they will fail in their duty over important ones, and once a principle is established its consequences must be accepted. However, I know for certain that down there they have only commanded the institution of this examination half-heartedly . . . you understand me . . . that secret protocol . . . concerning Mastro Germano.'

'If only the Chancellor were here . . .' murmured the Count of Fratta, a ray of hope lighting up his face.

'No, no. I don't wish, nor do I wish you to talk openly of this examination,' broke in the Venchieredo. 'It is enough for me to have reminded you, and to have proved to you, that it was not for suspicion against me, nor for the matter in itself, but simply as a principle of good government, that this decree was issued. . . . There is no longer any use in dragging this matter on. In fact, even at Venice they will not be displeased to see the whole thing cut short; it always happens that in actual application it is better to soften and smooth what seems too rough and too general in the maxims of state. Now, Signor Count, it is up to us, as between good friends, to interpret the hidden intentions of the Most Serene Inquisitors. The spirit, as you know even better than I, goes beyond the letter; and I assure you that even if the letter commands us to go on, the spirit counsels us to put a stop to all this. In confidence, I have even had communications from Venice to this effect and you may already guess the means . . . by an honest compromise . . . by some good half-measure, if needs be. . . .'

The Count opened his eyes still wider and tugged with his fingers at the lace of his shirt; at this point all the breath that he had kept bottled up in his chest because of his great agitation rushed out noisily in a great snort.

'Oh, don't upset yourself for that!' went on the other. 'The matter is easier than you think. And even were it very difficult, one would have to try and obey the spirit of the Most Serene Council of Ten. The spirit, remember well, not the letter! . . . Since the justice of the Most Serene Republic cannot desire that a most excellent Signor, such as you, should find himself in grave embarrassment because he felt too much bound by the apparent meaning of a decree. Think of it! To put a magistrate at loggerheads with all his colleagues! . . . It would be ingratitude, it would be unpardonable wickedness towards you.'

The poor magistrate understood, with the acumen of fear, only too well what all this was aiming at, and the cold sweat began to form on his temples like the drops from a taper on processional days. The necessity of replying, of saying either yes or no, was such a torture for him that he would have preferred to cede all his rights of jurisdiction to be released from it. But at last it seemed to him that he had found the best way of extricating himself! Imagine what talent! . . . Really he had hit upon a great novelty!

'But . . . in time . . . we shall see . . . we shall arrange something!'

172

'Egyptian darkness!' the Venchieredo leapt up in a fine fury. 'Who has time needs not wait for time, dearest Count! I, for example, if I were you, would say at once and for my own good reasons: "To-morrow there shall be no more talk of this examination!"'

'But how? How is that possible?' exclaimed the Count of Fratta.

'Ah, I see we are beginning to understand one another again,' said the other. 'He who looks for means is already persuaded of the greatest. And the means are already to hand. Everything is in order, Signor Count, for you to be disposed to satisfy, as is your need, the secret desires of the Council of Ten and mine also.'

That *mine* was pronounced in a way that reminded one of the discharge of a blunderbuss.

'But surely . . . I am very well disposed to . . .' stammered the poor man. 'When you assure me that even those above us so desire. . . .'

'Certainly, for the lesser evil,' went on the Venchieredo. 'It being always understood that everything must take place as if by chance. That is the knot in the skein. One good word to Germano, you understand me! . . . And a touch of hot steel on those papers, and that is the last that we shall hear of it. . . .'

'But the Chancellor . . . ?'

'He will not speak, be easy on that score! I have a word for him also. Thus it is desired by those who stand high, and thus too I desire it; not that the matter could have any consequences to harm me; but I should grieve to have to make reprisals against a man of his merit. The castellan of Venchieredo to undergo a trial instituted by one of his peers! Imagine it! I should myself insist that such a trial be held elsewhere; at Udine, at Venice, where you will, then I should clear myself, then I should defend myself. Here, as you can see well, it would be impossible; I cannot allow it at the cost of killing not one but a thousand.'

The Count of Fratta trembled from head to foot, but by this

173

time he was getting accustomed to these sudden assaults and found breath to remark:

'Very well, Your Excellency, and if it should not be found possible to send these inconclusive papers to Venice?'

'Bah!' the Venchieredo hastened to interrupt him. 'Have I not told you that, being inconclusive, there is no need to worry the postal authorities about them?'

'Since that is so,' replied the Count in a low tone, 'since that is so, let us burn them . . . to-morrow . . .'

'We will burn them at once,' broke in the castellan, rising.

'At once? . . . At once, you say? . . .' The Count raised his eyes, since he did not at that moment feel the least desire to get out of his chair. But one must suppose that the face of his interlocutor must have been very expressive, since he added immediately: 'Yes, yes, you are right! . . . They shall be burnt at once, at once!'

With a great effort he rose to his feet and moved towards the door, no longer even conscious of the world around him. But as his hand was on the latch a modest and whining voice was heard asking: 'With permission?' and the humble Fulgenzio entered the room with a paper in his hand.

'What is it? What do you want? Who told you to come in?' asked his patron, trembling all over.

'The Serjeant has brought this most urgent message from Portogruaro, from the Most Serene Signoria,' replied Fulgenzio.

'Leave it. Leave it till to-morrow!' replied the Venchieredo, who had gone a little pale and had moved towards the threshold.

'Your Excellency will excuse me,' replied Fulgenzio. 'The order is peremptory. It must be read at once.'

'Alas, yes . . . I will read it immediately,' said the Count, putting on his spectacles and unsealing the message. But hardly had he set eyes on it than such a tremor ran through his person that he had to support himself by a chair in order to maintain control of his legs. At the same time the Venchieredo scanned the piece of parchment and got a hint of its contents.

174

'I see that we shall not come to an understanding to-day, Signor Count!' he said with all his usual arrogance. 'I recommend you to the protection of the Council of Ten and of St. Anthony. I remain with the pleasure of having made my bow to you.'

Saying which, he went down the stairs, leaving the Magistrate of Fratta quite bemused.

'Ah, so? . . . You are going?' said the Count when he had recovered from his bewilderment.

'Yes, Excellency! He has gone,' replied Fulgenzio.

'Look, just look what they have written to me!' the Count went on, handing the message to the sacristan.

Fulgenzio read without surprise a formal order to arrest the Signor of Venchieredo whenever occasion offered to do so without causing an uproar.

'Now he has gone, he has really gone, and it is not my fault that I did not stop him,' said the Count. 'You are witness that he had gone before I was able to understand the meaning of the message.'

'Your Excellency, I will be witness of whatever you command!'

'It would perhaps have been better if the Serjeant had delayed another half-hour!'

Fulgenzio smiled to himself; and the Count went in search of the Chancellor to share with him this new and even more terrible complication in which they were now embroiled.

Who Fulgenzio was and what was his office, you can imagine as well as I can; there were frequent similar cases, in which the Signoria of Venice made use of the most abject servants to watch over the fidelity and zeal of their masters. As to Venchieredo, despite his apparent arrogance, he had had a great shock as he read that message. He had at once understood that they were going to settle with him mercilessly, since the arguments of fear are ever victorious. But a little after, he regained confidence in his own wiliness, in his exalted relations and in the weakness of the government, and again thought of attempting to escape. His first plan was to slip over into Illyria; and

175

we shall see later whether he would have been right or not in that decision. Then he reflected that it would not be easy to capture him without causing a great uproar and, at the worst, he would be able to slip across the Isonzo at any time it seemed expedient to him. The desire to revenge himself by a single blow on Fulgenzio, the Chaplain, the Spaccafumo, the Count and even to make the Most Supreme Signoria come to their senses, finally decided this ferocious and turbulent spirit. He remained, therefore, constrained by fear to an even greater temerity.

# V

IT is with the story of my life as I believe it is with that of others. It departs solitary from the cradle, only later to become involved with, wander among, and be confounded with the infinite multitude of human affairs, to return solitary and rich only in sorrows and memories to the peace of the grave. Thus the irrigation channels of well-watered Lombardy emerge from some Alpine lake or some river of the plain, to divide, sub-divide and break into a hundred brooks, a thousand runnels and streams; further down, the waters meet again in a single slow-moving stream, pale and silent, which breaks into the Po.

Is it a merit or a fault? Modesty would that I should call it merit; since my affairs would be very unimportant and my opinions and changes and conversations unworthy of study were they not interwoven with the stories of other men who found themselves in the same path and with whom I was for a time a fellow traveller in this world's pilgrimage. But would these then be my confessions? Or shall I not seem rather like the village flirt who, instead of her own sins, tells the priest those of her husband or sister-in-law, or the gossip of the countryside? Patience! Man is so bound to the century in which he lives that he cannot declare his own soul without examining also the husks of the generation that enfolds him. As the thoughts of time and space are lost in the infinite, so man is lost on every side in the tide of humanity. The barriers of egoism, of interest and of religion are not enough; our philosophy may be right in practice, but the inexorable wisdom of primitive India takes revenge upon our arrogant little systems in the full truth of the eternal metaphysic.

Meanwhile, you will have noticed that in this account of my childhood my personages have so multiplied about me as to cause real alarm. I am myself dismayed by them, like that witch who was frightened by the devils she had so imprudently invoked. It is a real phalanx that pretends to walk with me and much hinders with its noise and chatter my haste to press onward. But do not doubt; life is not a pitched battle but rather a continuous development of skirmishes and daily forays. The phalanx does not fall in ranks as under the fire of cannon, but is broken and decimated by desertion, by ambush and by epidemic. The companions of our youth leave us one by one and abandon us to the new friendships, infrequent, cautious and self-interested, of maturity. From thence to the desert of old age is but a short step filled with lamentations and with tears. Give time to time, my sons! After having passed with me through the gay, varied and populous labyrinth of my green years, you will end by sitting in an armchair whence the poor old man can only just move and confides himself, by the aid of courage and meditation, to the future that extends beyond the tomb. But for the moment, let me show you the old world; that world that went its childish way at the end of last century, before the magic breath of the French revolution rejuvenated it in body and in spirit. The men of that time were not as those of to-day; look well at them and see in them a mirror to imitate their little good and to correct their much evil. I, the relict of that covey, have the right to speak clearly; you have the right of judgement and you will use it after I have spoken.

I no longer recall how many, but certainly very few, days after the meeting of the castellan of Venchieredo with the Count, the district of Fratta was disturbed towards evening by an unexpected invasion. They were rustics and smugglers who were running away pell-mell and after them Cernide, buli and a posse of serjeants, bullying the peasants whom they met and creating the greatest uproar that could be imagined. At the first sound of this rabble, the Countess, who had gone out with Monsignor de Sant'Andrea and Rosa for her afternoon walk, at once shut herself up in the castle and caused her husband to be woken up to find out what this new development was.

The Count, who for the past week had only been able to sleep with one eye shut, descended precipitously to the kitchen

178

and in a short time the Chancellor, Monsignor Orlando, Marchetto, Fulgenzio, the bailiff and the Captain had gathered about him with the most dismayed faces in the world. By now each of them had understood that they could not so easily recover their one-time calm, and at every new sign of commotion their fears redoubled, as the symptoms of a relapse redouble in the soul of a convalescent. That evening it was up to Captain Sandracca and three of his assistants to show their lion hearts and go out into the open. But not five minutes had passed before they returned with their tails between their legs and with no desire to repeat the experiment.

The rabble that was rioting in the public square was made up of the posse of Venchieredo and showed no disposition to withdraw. Gaetano, at the staff headquarters of the inn, swore and forswore that he would tear the smugglers into pieces and that those who had taken refuge in the castle would pay even more heavily than the others. He pretended that here in the district there was a confederation to defraud the revenue and that the Chancellor and the Count were its ringleaders. The moment had come, he said, to exterminate this band, and if he who was supposed to be the guardian of the laws had become their most open enemy, it was their duty to carry out the decrees of the Most Serene Signoria and acquire great merit by this enterprise.

'Germano! Germano! Pull up the drawbridge and bar the doors well!' screamed the Count after he had heard all this long-winded talk of insults and fables.

'I have already lifted the drawbridge, Your Excellency,' replied the Captain, 'and for greater security I have had it thrown into the moat by three of my men, because the pulleys would not work.'

'Excellent, excellent! Bar the windows and put padlocks on all the exits,' added the Count. 'Nobody must dare to stir a foot outside the castle. . . .'

'I defy anyone to move now that the bridge has been destroyed,' observed the Serjeant.

'It seems to me that the small bridge by the stables would

179

assure a sortie in case of necessity,' the Captain added sagaciously.

'No, no, I want no sorties!' the Count shouted. 'Throw down
the little bridge by the stables as well, at once; from now on, I
put my castle in a state of siege and of defence.'

'I would like to observe to Your Excellency that once this
bridge has been destroyed, there will be no way to get out to
collect the daily provisions,' objected the bailiff with a deep bow.

'No matter! My husband is right,' replied the Countess, who
was the most frightened of all. 'Your place is to obey and to
demolish the bridge by the stables immediately; there is no
time to lose! We might be assassinated at any moment!'

The bailiff bowed even more deeply and went to carry out
the task assigned to him. A quarter of an hour later all communications between the Castle of Fratta and the rest of the
world had been completely cut off and the Count and Countess
breathed more freely. Only Monsignor Orlando, who was certainly no hero, risked showing a little anxiety about the difficulty of obtaining the usual quantity of beef and veal for the
morrow. The Signor Count, hearing the remonstrances of his
brother, now had the chance to show his acumen and the
readiness of his administrative genius.

'Fulgenzio,' he said in a solemn voice, 'how many little ones
has your sow in her litter?'

'Ten, Excellency,' replied the sacristan.

'Then we are provided for a whole week,' replied the Count,
'since the fishpond will provide us for the two fast days.'

Monsignor Orlando sighed, sorrowfully recalling the fine
oradas of Marano and the succulent eels of Caorle. Alas, what
in comparison with these were the muddy carp and the frogs
of the fishpond?

'Fulgenzio,' the Count meanwhile went on, 'have two of your
piglets killed, one for boiling and one for roasting; have you
understood, Margherita?'

Fulgenzio and the cook bowed; but it was now the turn of
Monsignor de Sant'Andrea, who because of an intestinal complaint was unable to digest pork, and the perspective of a week

180

of siege with such a régime did not suit him at all. However, the Countess, who had read the discontent in his face, hastened to assure him that a pullet would be set aside to boil for him. The features of the canon cleared to a holy tranquillity, for with a good pullet even a week of siege seemed to him a very moderate purgatory.

After the orders had been given to the kitchen staff, the garrison dispersed to put the castle in a state of defence. Some old muskets were placed in the loop-holes and two long-disused saluting pieces were dragged into the first courtyard; the doors and balconies were barred. Finally the bell was rung for the Rosary and none of them ever said it with greater devotion than on that evening. The Countess meanwhile had been too distracted to pay attention to anyone save herself, but her mother-in-law, as soon as it began to grow dark, asked about Clara, for she was so late in bringing her bread and milk. Faustina, the Pisana and I set ourselves immediately to look for her; calling here, running there, we could find her nowhere. The gardener told us he had seen her go out by way of the stables a couple of hours before, but he knew nothing more and believed that she had returned, as usual, with the Signora Contessa.

She certainly would not now have been able to return the way she went, for the bailiff had carried out his orders with such despatch that not a trace remained of the little bridge.

Besides, night had already fallen; it was very dark and not to be thought that she was still walking around outside.

We began looking for her all over again and only after another hour of close and fruitless search Faustina decided to go back to the kitchen and tell her masters the sad news of the disappearance of the Contessina.

'Giurabacco!' exclaimed the Count, 'those scoundrels have certainly carried her off!'

The Countess tried to show great distress, but her anxiety about herself kept her too preoccupied to succeed.

'Just think,' went on her husband, 'just think what those wretches are capable of doing, since they dare to call me a

181

smuggler to put the whole countryside in disorder. But they'll pay me for this, they'll pay me for this!' he added in a low voice in fear lest someone outside his little circle should hear him.

'Talk, talk!' broke in the Countess. 'It's all very well for you to talk and meanwhile it is we who are being fried! Here we are already three hours in this net and you haven't even thought of any way to get us out of the mess. They carry off our daughter and you waste your breath in saying that they will pay you for it! . . . For all that's worth, you could claim little enough!'

'But, wife! . . . For all that's worth? . . . What do you mean?'

'Eh, if you don't understand me, sharpen your wits. I mean to say that you have been thinking about our children, about me myself and about our salvation, about as much as straightening the bell-tower.' Here the Countess angrily took a pinch of snuff. 'Let us see. What have you thought about getting us out of this mess? How do you intend to go and look for Clara?'

'Be reasonable, *diamine*! . . . Clara! Clara! There is no reason to go up in the air like that. You know how quiet and well bred she is. Even if she does sleep a night outside the castle, I don't see why any harm should come to her. As for us, I hope you don't want it to come to shooting.' The Countess made a gesture of fright and impatience. 'Well,' went on her husband, 'we shall try to parley.'

'To parley with thieves! A good idea, indeed!'

'Thieves! . . . Who said they were thieves? . . . They are organs of justice, a little over-hasty, a little drunk, if you like, but none the less invested with a legal authority, and once their madness has passed they will listen to reason. They have become rather over-eager in hunting down one or two smugglers, the wine has gone to their heads and they have got the idea that the fugitives have taken refuge at Fratta. What is there strange in that? . . . If we persuade them there are no smugglers here, nor ever have been, they will go back home as quiet as lambs.'

'Excellency, you are forgetting one thing,' interrupted

182

Monsignor de Sant'Andrea. 'It seems that these fugitives are assassins disguised as smugglers and are being hunted merely as a pretext to create this disorder. Germano says that he has recognized amongst them some of the moustachioed bravos of Venchieredo.'

'But how do I come into all this? What has it to do with me?' the poor Count exclaimed in despair.

'One might send someone out secretly to try and see how things are and look for news of the Contessina,' advised the Serjeant.

'Oh, oh!' replied the Countess, feebly. 'That would be a great imprudence, since we are so short of men in the castle. This is not the time to send any of the best of them away.'

The Pisana, who was squatting with me between Martino's knees, advanced boldly towards the hearth and offered to go and look for her sister; but they were all so terrified that nobody but Marchetto seemed to take any notice of this childish and moving temerity. But her offer was not without result as, after the Pisana, I too offered to go out and look for the Contessina. This time the suggestion had the good fortune to attract someone's attention.

'Would you really take the risk of going out to have a look around?' the bailiff asked me.

'Yes, certainly,' I said, raising my head and looking proudly at the Pisana.

'Let's go together,' said the little girl, who did not want to appear less daring than I.

'Oh no, these are not matters for little girls,' said the bailiff, 'but Carlino here would wriggle easily out of any difficulty. Isn't it true, Signora Contessa? The idea is quite a good one.'

'For lack of a better, I won't deny it,' replied the Countess. 'Here, inside, a boy would be of little use to us, but outside he would not be suspected and could push his nose in anywhere. Also he can be as malicious and bold as the devil himself, as we already know.'

'But I want to go too! I want to go and look for Clara too!' the Pisana began to scream.

183

'You, miss, will go to bed at once,' replied the Countess and motioned to Faustina to put the command into immediate effect.

Then there was a little battle of howls, scratches and bites, but the maid won, and the desperate little being was taken fairly and squarely to bed.

'What must I tell the old Countess about the Contessina Clara?' the woman asked as she was going away with the Pisana in her arms.

'Say she is lost, that she cannot be found, that she will be back to-morrow!' replied the Countess.

'If I may be permitted to advise, it would be better to say that her aunt from Cisterna has come to take her away,' suggested the bailiff.

'Yes, yes, make her believe some story or other!' exclaimed the Countess, 'not to worry her, since we have quite enough troubles already.'

Faustina went out, and the cries of the Pisana could be heard diminishing along the corridor.

'Now attend to me, little serpent,' said the bailiff, taking me roughly by the ear. 'Let us hear. What good will you be to us once you are outside the castle?'

'I . . . I will just take a walk round the countryside a little,' I suggested, 'and then, as if there was nothing the matter, I would drop in at the inn, where all these gentry are, to weep and complain that I can't get back again into the castle. I will say that I went out with the Contessina Clara and then lost my way chasing butterflies and wasn't able to find her again. Then, if any of them knows anything about her, they will surely tell me and I will come back here and whistle behind the stables. The gardener will push a table across to me and I will come back across the moat in the same way as I went out.'

'Wonderful! You are a real paladin,' replied the bailiff.

'What is all this about?' Martino asked me. He was quite confused by all this talking that he saw me doing without being able to understand a word of it.

'I am going out to look for the Contessina, who has not yet come back,' I shouted at the top of my voice.

'Yes, yes, you are doing very well,' said the old man, 'but be very careful.'

'And don't compromise us . . .' continued the Countess.

'It would be a good thing if you could overhear something of what these assassins are saying at the inn, so that we can know their intentions,' added the Count. 'In that way we shall know what to do later.'

'Yes, yes, and come back quickly, little one,' went on the Countess, caressing me by that unfortunate lock of hair that had so many times experienced a different fate. 'Go, look, observe and tell us faithfully all about it! The Good Lord has made you so cunning and resolute for our greater good! . . . Go, and may the Lord bless you! And remember that we are all waiting for you here with anxious hearts.'

'I will come back as soon as I have smelt out something,' I replied with an air of importance, since I felt myself the only man in that warren of rabbits.

Marchetto, the bailiff and Martino came to me, encouraging me and recommending me to be prudent, wary and careful. A table was pushed into the moat and I, who was skilful enough in this manner of navigation, reached the further bank successfully and with a push sent my vessel back to them. Thence, while on the advice of Monsignor Orlando, a second Rosary was intoned in the castle, I set out among the deep shadows of the night on my courageous expedition.

Clara, meanwhile, had gone out by the postern before vespers, as the gardener had said, and had not returned. She had expected to meet her mother along the Fossalta road and so, step by step, had reached that village without coming across anyone. Then she thought that it must be later than usual and that the band from the castle must have turned back while she was making the detour round the vegetable garden to the road. Therefore she too turned hastily back to return to the castle, but she had not walked more than a stone's throw when

185

the sound of footsteps made her turn round. It was Lucilio; Lucilio calm and pensive as ever, but irradiated at that moment by an ill-concealed joy that perhaps he did not even try to conceal.

Nothing will ever satisfy the speed of thought; the steamship seems too slow and one day even electricity will seem more idle and tedious than a carriage horse. Believe me, it will be so, and in the final analysis the proportions will remain the same, though as if in the magnified circle of a spy-glass. The mind divines about itself a world very high, distant and inaccessible, and every turn, every step, every spiral that moves or stirs without approaching that dreamed-of Paradise will not seem like motion, but torpor and tedium. What use is it to go from Milan to Paris in thirty-six hours rather than two hundred? What use is it to be able to see the four quarters of the world ten times in forty years rather than once? Neither the world grows larger nor life longer for that, and whoever thinks much will always run beyond those limits into the infinite, into the mystery without light.

To Clara and Lucilio this moment that they were one beside the other seemed very long, while the time from their meeting as they walked together to the first houses of Fratta passed in a flash. Though their feet advanced lingeringly, even without noticing it, they stopped many times along the way, talking of the old Countess, of the castellan of Venchieredo, of their opinions about him, and even more frequently about themselves and their own feelings, of the most beautiful sky that enchanted them, and of the lovely sunset that made them halt for a long time to watch in ecstasy.

'That is how I would like to live,' exclaimed Clara ingenuously.

'How? Tell me quickly!' said Lucilio in his gentlest voice. 'Let me see if I am able to understand your desires and take my share in them.'

'In truth I said I would like to live like that,' replied Clara. 'But now I don't know how to explain myself. I would like to live with this splendid light of the sky in my eyes, this gay

186

and harmonious peace that enfolds Nature as she falls asleep in my ears, and in my heart and spirit those sweet thoughts of brotherhood, those great feelings without distraction and without measure, that are born from the spectacle of simple and sublime things!'

'You would like to live that life that Nature has prepared for wise, equal and innocent men!' replied Lucilio sorrowfully. 'The life that in our words is known as dream and poetry. Oh yes! I understand it very well because I too breathe the fragrant air of dreams and put my trust in the poetry of hope, so as not to reply to injustice with hatred and to sorrow with desperation. Consider how ill-adjusted we are. Who has arms has no brains, who has brains has no heart, and who has both heart and brains has not authority. God is above us and we call Him just and all-seeing. We, the children of God, blind, unjust and oppressed, deny Him every moment with our words, our writings and our deeds. We deny His providence, His justice, His omnipotence! It is a sorrow vast as the world, continuing through the centuries, that forces us on, that pursues us and confounds us, and one day makes us recollect that we are all equal, but only in death! . . .'

'In death, in death? Say rather in life, the true life that will last for ever,' exclaimed Clara as if inspired. 'Behold where God rises again and is justified despite all the contradictions here below.'

'God must be everywhere,' went on Lucilio in a voice in which one who was devout might have desired a greater warmth of faith. But Clara did not feel that lack and he already knew that it would be so, otherwise he would not have spoken.

'Yes, God is everywhere!' she replied with an angelic smile, looking at the heavens above her. 'Can't you see Him, can't you hear Him, breathe Him everywhere? Pure thoughts, tender feelings, gentle passions, whence come they if not from Him? . . . Oh, I love God as the fountain of every beauty and every good!'

If ever any argument could have converted an unbeliever, it

was certainly the divine expression that at that moment spread over Clara's face. Immortality was emblazoned on that serene and confident forehead; certainly no one would have dared to say that such intelligence, feeling and beauty had been provided by Nature merely to serve as a pasture for worms. There are, indeed, dead, stony faces, twisted sensual expressions, bowed and fawning men who justify by their foul examples the terrible speculations of the materialists, who must be denied the eternity of the spirit as are animals or plants. But amid this moribund rabble there may arise some brow that seems illuminated by a supernatural radiance, and before such as these the cynic stutters confused words but cannot prevent a tremor at his heart of hope or of terror of a future life. What life, ask the philosophers? Do not ask me, if it is your misfortune not to be satisfied with that ancient, secret wisdom that is faith. Ask yourselves. But it is certain that if organic matter once divorced from its human conception ferments and lives again materially in the womb of earth, so the thinking spirit must live spiritually in the sea of thought. The movement that never ceases in the weary labour of the veins or the nerves, can it go back and find peace in the indefatigable and subtle element of ideas?

Lucilio gazed at the countenance of his companion with enraptured eyes. Then a gleam of light lit up his face and for the first time a sentiment not purely selfish but inspired by the feelings of another penetrated the dark recesses of his heart. But he recovered swiftly from this brief defeat to become once more master of himself.

'Divine poetry!' he said, turning his eyes from the lovely sunset that was just losing its colours in a vague twilight, ' . . . he who first soared with you in infinite hope was the true consoler of humanity. To teach men happiness, one must educate poets, not scientists or anatomists.'

Clara smiled compassionately and asked him:

'Then you, Signor Lucilio, are not very happy?'

'Yes, yes, I am now, as perhaps I could never be!' exclaimed the young man pressing one of her hands involuntarily. At this

188

clasp there vanished from the girl's face that immortal splendour of faith and a tender and tremulous light of feeling spread over it, like a lovely moonlight after the evening darkening of the sun. 'Yes, I am happy, as perhaps I never shall be again!' went on Lucilio. 'Happy in my desires, for my desires are full of hope and hope beckons to me from afar off like a lovely garden in full bloom. Ah me, do not pluck its flowers! I do not break them from their delicate stalks! For all the care we give them now, they will wither after three days, and after five they will no longer keep their lovely colours and their sweet perfume. In the end they will fall inevitably into the sepulchre of memory!'

'No, do not call memory a sepulchre!' rejoined Clara fervently. 'Memory is a temple, an altar! The bones of the saints that we venerate are underground, but their virtues shine in heaven. The flower loses its freshness and its perfume, but the memory of the flower remains in our soul, incorruptible and fragrant for ever!'

'My God, for ever, for ever!' exclaimed Lucilio, carried onward by the strength of his feelings towards the opportunity of those fateful moments. 'Yes, for ever! Be it an instant, a year, an eternity, this must always fill it, satisfy it, beautify it with love, so that it is no longer one with death. Ah yes, Clara, love returns to the infinite in every way; if there is a part of us that is sublime and immortal, it is certainly this. Let us trust in Him that we may not become callous before our time, that we may not lose at least this instinctive poetry of the soul that alone makes our life beautiful! . . . Yes, I swear it now, I swear it and I will always remember this rapture that raises me above myself. Desire may thus be transformed into faith; our love will last for ever because these things that are really great can never come to an end! . . .'

These words pronounced by the young man in a subdued, yet deep and vibrant voice, awakened to delight the confused desires of Clara. It was no wonder, since for a long time past the things that she heard then had been stirring in her heart. The looks, the words, the patient and subtle arts of Lucilio had

189

prepared a sure place in her soul for this ardent declaration. To hear repeated by his lips what her heart had unconsciously been long awaiting was like the sudden awakening of a timid and latent joy. There took place in her soul what takes place on a photographic plate when it is placed in the acid; the hidden image is developed in all its forms, and if one cannot wonder at that moment, it is perhaps because one is incapable of wonder. A secret and hitherto unfelt agitation prevented her from replying to the ardent words of the young man and as she tried to withdraw her hand from his she was forced to seek a support as she felt overcome by a delicious swoon of pleasure.

'Clara, Clara, please answer me!' Lucilio begged, supporting her in anguish and looking around to see if anyone were coming. 'Answer me only one word! . . . Don't kill me with your silence, don't punish me with the sight of your grief! Pardon me! If nothing else, pardon me!'

He seemed almost as if he would fall on his knees, so overcome he appeared, but it was a studied attitude, perhaps to hasten the moment. Clara recovered herself and gave him for sole response a smile. Who could have seen such a smile and not have remembered it for all his life? That smile that asks compassion, that promises felicity, that says all, that pardons all; that smile that portrays a soul that gives itself to another soul, that has not in itself any reflexion of the images of this world, that shines only with love and for love; that smile that understands, or better forgets, the whole world, to live and let you live by it alone and that in a single flash reveals its love and confounds the mysterious depths of two spirits in a single desire of love and eternity, in a single feeling of beatitude and of faith! The heaven that opens full of visions and ineffable splendour to the eyes of a saint would not surely be more enchanting than this flash of felicity that sparkles radiant and, alas, too fleeting in the face of a woman. It is a meteor, it is a flash, but in this flash, sooner than in ten years of meditation and study, the soul sees instinctively the confused horizons of a future life. Oh, how often in the clouding of these faces is quenched within us the lovely serenity of hope, and thought

190

throws us down blaspheming into the great emptiness of the void, like the doomed Icarus, whose wings of wax melted! What sudden, sorrowful beating of the useless ether, where myriads of spirits swim in the oceans of light, to the dread and chill abyss wherein no ray of sun is ever seen, that will never more give life through the turning of the centuries to the shadow of a dream! Science, the heir of a hundred generations, and pride, the fruit of four thousand years of history, flee like slaves caught in ill-doing before the menacing onslaught of such a feeling. What are we, where are we going, poor straying pilgrims? Where is the guide that assures us of a not unhappy voyage? A thousand voices sound about us; a hundred mysterious hands beckon us to paths still more mysterious; a secret and fatal force presses us onwards to right or to left; love, the winged boy, invites us to Paradise; love, the mocking demon, destroys us in the void. And only the belief that our sacrifices will lessen the sufferings of others, sustains us.

But Lucilio? . . . Lucilio was not thinking of that then. Thought follows after joy, as the night the twilight, or the chill winter the golden and harmonious autumn. He had loved for years; for years he had directed his every counsel, his every art, his every word, to create, in a distant future, the beatitude of that moment; for years he had walked patiently and warily, by tortuous and solitary ways, lit now and again by some flash of hope; he had moved onward slowly and tirelessly towards that flowered height, whence he then surveyed and held for his own all the joys, all the delights, all the riches of this world, as master of the universe. He had been able to create the philosophers' stone; by a laborious mixture of looks, of actions, of words, he had extracted the purest gold of felicity and love. Victorious alchemist, he savoured with all his senses the delights of triumph; enthusiastic and passionate artist, he never ceased admiring and enjoying his own creation in that divine smile that broke out on Clara's face like the dawn of a still more beautiful day. Others would have felt their hearts tremble with gratitude; in him, pride tempered once more the

191

fibres of an unbridled and tyrannical joy. I perhaps, and a thousand others like me, would have given thanks with tears in our eyes; he rewarded the submission of Clara with a fiery kiss.

'You are mine! You are mine!' he said, raising her hand to the sky. And he wished to imply: 'I deserve you, because I have conquered you.'

Clara said nothing in reply. She had loved him till then without realizing it and without revealing it, and the moment in which love is conscious of itself is not the moment for speech. She only felt herself to be for the first time utterly in the power of another, and that feeling did no more than change her smile from the colour of joy to that of hope. At the first moment she had rejoiced for herself; now she rejoiced for Lucilio, and this joy was easier and dearer to her, since it was more modest and more compassionate.

'Clara,' went on Lucilio, 'it is getting late and they will be expecting us at the castle.'

The young girl started as if from a dream, wiped her eyes with her hand and felt them bathed with tears.

'Shall we go?' she replied in a sweet subdued voice that scarcely seemed her own. Lucilio without a word set out again along the road and the girl walked by his side, quiet and gentle as a lamb by the side of its mother. For that day, the young man asked no more. The treasure once revealed, he wanted to enjoy it for long, like a miser; not to squander it madly in prodigies, only to find himself afterwards in greater misery than before, with the added burden of vanished memories.

'Will you love me always?' he asked her, after a few steps in silence.

'Always,' she replied. An angel's harp never made sweeter sound than that word, pronounced by such lips. Love has the genius of Paganini; it confounds in harmony the virtues of the spirit.

'And when your family finds a husband for you?' added Lucilio in a harsh and mournful voice.

'A husband?' echoed the girl, drooping her head.

192

'Yes,' replied the youth. 'They will sacrifice you to ambition, they will ask of you in the name of religion a love that religion will forbid you in the name of nature.'

'Oh, I will never look at anyone but you!' replied Clara, almost as if talking to herself.

'Swear it by all you hold most sacred! Swear it by your God and the life of your grandmother!' exclaimed Lucilio.

'Yes, I swear it!' Clara replied calmly. To swear what she felt herself impelled to do by an irresistible force seemed to her quite simple and natural. Then they began to see through the evening shadows the first houses of Fratta, and Lucilio released the girl's hand to walk respectfully by her side. But the die had been cast; their two souls were joined for ever. Perseverance and reserve on the one hand, gentleness and compassion on the other, had merged them in a flame of love. The resolution of Lucilio and the self-denial of Clara corresponded, like twin stars eternally drawing nearer to one another in the spaces of the sky.

Two armed men came to meet them at the entrance of the village. Lucilio passed them by, thinking they were two rural guards who were on the look-out for someone; but one of them ordered him to halt, saying that on that evening entry into the district was forbidden. The young man was offended and surprised at such unusual temerity and adopted a method that he knew from much experience to be infallible in such encounters. He began to raise his voice and abuse them. But in vain. The two buli held him respectfully by the arms, replying that the service of the Most Serene Signoria so demanded, and that no one could enter Fratta until the search for certain smugglers they were looking for had been completed.

'I presume you will not prevent the Contessina Clara from entering the castle?' replied Lucilio, fuming with rage and pointing to the young girl whom he was accompanying, holding her arm tightly. Clara made a movement as if to restrain him from getting too angry, but he paid no attention and went on threatening and trying to go onwards. The two buli still held him by the arms and warned him that their orders were

193

precise and that they had the right to use force against anyone disobeying them.

'That right to use force I have too, and I make great use of it against impudent fellows!' went on Lucilio still more heatedly, loosing himself with a blow from the two rascals. But a movement from Clara warned him of his danger and the unseasonableness of such acts of violence. He calmed once more and asked the two who they were and on what authority they forbade entry to the castle to the daughter of the Magistrate. The men replied that they were Cernide from Venchieredo, but that their pursuit of the smugglers authorized them to act outside their own jurisdiction if necessary, that the ban of the Signor Syndics spoke clearly and that, furthermore, those were the orders of the Captain of a Hundred, and they were only there to see that they were carried out. Lucilio could have protested further but Clara begged him gently to stop, so he contented himself with turning back with her and threatening the two rascals and their masters with all the thunders of the Viceroy and the Most Serene Signoria, of whose small value he was very well aware.

'Be quiet! It is useless,' Clara whispered in his ear, dragging him away from the two guards. 'I'm sorry that it is night already and they will be anxious about me at home, but with a little detour we shall easily be able to get in by the stables.'

They started to walk across the fields, looking for the path that led to the postern, but they had not gone a hundred paces before they encountered two more guards.

'It's a real ambush!' exclaimed Lucilio angrily. 'Must a young noblewoman spend all night out at the caprice of a few scoundrels?'

'Watch your words, illustrissimo,' shouted one of them, giving a tremendous thump on the ground with the butt of his musket.

The young man trembled with rage and felt with one hand in his pocket for his faithful pistol, but with the other one he felt Clara's arm trembling with fright and had the forbearance to restrain himself.

194

'Let us try to come to an understanding . . .' he replied, still fuming with rage. 'How much do you want to let the Contessina pass? I assume you do not suspect her of bringing any contraband!'

'Illustrissimo, we suspect nothing,' replied the guard, 'but even if we could shut an eye and let her pass, those in the castle are of different opinion. They have destroyed both the bridges and the Contessina could only enter by walking on the water like St. Peter!'

'Then the danger really must be serious,' said Clara faintly.

'It's nothing. They have got into a panic, or so I suppose,' replied Lucilio. Turning once more to the guard, he asked: 'Where is your Captain of a Hundred?'

' 'Lustrissimo, he is drinking of the best at the inn, while we are here keeping watch on the bats,' replied the man.

'Very well. I hope at least you will not refuse to accompany us to the inn to talk to him,' suggested Lucilio.

'Well, we have no orders about that . . .' responded the other. 'However, it seems all right to me, especially if Your Honour will pay for a glass or two.'

'Come along then, come with us,' said Lucilio.

The guard turned to his companion, telling him to remain at his post and not to go to sleep; warnings that were heard with very little satisfaction by the one who had to remain eating fog, while the other had in view a good flask of Cividino. However, he resigned himself, grumbling, and Lucilio and Clara, preceded by the guard, set out again across the fields.

This time the two guards let them pass and they were soon at the inn, where reigned such a commotion that it seemed more like a carnival than a chase for smugglers. Indeed Gaetano, after quenching the thirst of his own people, had begun to offer glasses to the onlookers. These, already a little unruly from the start, had by now come to the closest understanding with him in that mute and expressive language. Those who were drinking called for company, and as this grew they revived and drank still more. Thus, mingling and intermingling, at the end of half an hour the posse of Venchieredo

195

had become a single family with the peasants of the neighbourhood and the host never ceased praising to the skies the splendour and unusual correctness of the Captain of a Hundred of the Cernide of Venchieredo. As may well be believed, such munificence was neither arbitrary nor without its reason. The master had suggested to him that he should keep the local people quiet and prevent them from taking sides against them in favour of the castellans. Gaetano had worked cunningly and the aims of his chief had been well served. Had he wished, three hundred topers would have shouted 'Long live the castellan of Venchieredo!' And God knows what effect the menacing sound of such a shout would have had in the Castle of Fratta.

When Lucilio and Clara set foot in the inn the uproar was at its height. The young noblewoman was heart-broken at seeing their most loyal tenants joining in revelry with the enemies of her family; but they paid no heed to her and surprise and dismay at all this tumult prevented her from seeing clearly. She feared some serious peril for her family and was sorry she was not with them to share it, never thinking that their peril, protected as they were by a wide moat, was far less than her own, defended by a single man against this turbulent rabble.

Lucilio, however, was not of a spirit to be easily imposed upon by anyone. He went directly to Gaetano and ordered him, in a rather arrogant tone, to arrange for the Contessina's return to the castle. The truculence of the new arrival and the wine that he had drunk made the Captain of a Hundred even more above himself than ever. He replied that those in the castle were a perverse race of smugglers and that he had the task of keeping them shut up until they had handed over the guilty and returned the smuggled goods, and that as far as the Contessina was concerned, he had better look after her himself seeing that he had her on his arm. Lucilio lifted his fist to strike him for his impudence, but thought better of it and twirled his moustache furiously in the favourite gesture of Captain Sandracca. The only thing left to do was to get out of this turmoil and take his companion to some secure refuge where she could pass the night.

Clara at first protested against this decision and wanted at all costs to go as far as the bridge to see if it really had been destroyed. Lucilio accompanied her, even though it seemed dangerous to him to adventure abroad with the girl amongst the wine-sodden rascals who were rioting in the piazza. But he did not want to give her any occasion to think that he lacked courage or that he had omitted any chance of helping her to get home. However, after they had looked at the ruin of the bridge and had called vainly to Germano once or twice, they had to hasten to leave because the commotion continued to grow and the posse had begun to crowd around them and provoke them with jests and insults. Lucilio sweated at the necessity for showing moderation; but his principal duty was to keep the girl safe and with this in mind he went down a small byway in the village and turning towards the Venchieredo road soon arrived, hurrying Clara along with him, at the meadow of the mills.

There he stopped to let her get her breath. She sat down, weary and tearful, by a hedge and the young man bent over to look at her pale face, on which the light of the newly-risen moon seemed to be tenderly reflected. The dark buildings of the castle rose before them and an occasional light appeared between the chinks of the balconies only to be once more quickly concealed like stars in a stormy sky. The dark foliage of the poplars waved gently and the uproar of the village, deadened by distance, in no way interrupted the amorous outpourings of the nightingales. Fireflies shone in the grasses, the stars twinkled in the sky and the new moon striped the vague and shadowy forms around them with slanting, veiled rays. Modest Nature surrounded with darkness and silence her summer bridebed, but her throbbing heart was thrilled now and again by some breeze redolent of fruitfulness.

It was one of those hours in which man does not think, but feels; that is, he receives the thoughts and facts of the universe that absorbs him. Lucilio, a nature pensive and, above all, disdainful, felt small despite himself in a calm so solemn and profound. The joy of love diffused itself through his heart in vain

197

imaginings, melancholy and sweet. It seemed to him that his feelings grew like a cloud of dust dispersed by the wind; but their forms faded, their colour was dissipated; he felt greater and yet less strong, more master of all and less of himself. There seemed a moment when Clara, seated before him, was bathed in a flash of light and he himself, as if thunderstruck, had to close his eyes . . . whence this marvel? . . . He could not understand it himself. Perhaps the solemnity of the night, that binds weak souls with superstitious fears, yet reinforces the spirit of the strong, showed them in the darkness of its shadows the image of destiny, the subduer of all. Perhaps also he was affected by the girl's grief, even as a short time before he had triumphed over her by the force of his resolution. No, her eyes were not flashing then, unless it were with the shining of tears. Her heart, overflowing half an hour before with felicity and love, had flown now to the bedside of her grandmother, to that little neat and silent room where Lucilio had passed long hours with her and where, when he had gone away, there remained hovering in the air a dear memory, an invisible and enchanting memory. How could the poor old woman have managed to get to sleep without the customary kiss from her granddaughter? Who would have remembered her in the perils that menaced the castle that night?

Pity, divine pity, filled the girl's breast with fresh sobs and the hand that Lucilio took to help her rise was bathed in tears. But once more upon their way, Lucilio's usual alacrity returned. His dreams vanished, his thoughts sprang up once more, resolute and virile, and his mind, subdued for a moment, rose up with greater force to resume its command. The story of his and Clara's love, the extraordinary events of that night, the feelings of the young girl and his own, depicted themselves before him in a single picture clearly and in due order. He looked on them with an eagle's eye, seeing the whole scheme before him, and decided that at all costs, either alone or with the girl, he had to enter the castle before the night had passed. Love imposed on him this duty and let us add that the interest of his love also counselled him strongly. Clara prayed to God

198

and the Madonna. Lucilio summoned to his aid all the resources of his nature and his courage; and so, arm in arm, they
walked silently towards the mill. What moderation, some
would say, thinking of Lucilio. But if so, it is either that I have
explained badly or that they have not understood me properly
when I was speaking of his temperament. Lucilio was neither
a villain nor reckless; he only claimed to see to the depths of
human affairs, to desire the best in them and to know how to
obtain that best. These pretensions, when tempered by a sane
judgement, he could have proved by deeds, since he never
allowed himself to be carried away by his passions, but firmly
kept the reins and knew how to hold them at need even on the
brink of a precipice or on the flattering and treacherous bank of
some flowering mead.

The two entered the mill but found nobody there, though
fire was still flickering among the embers in the hearth. The
polenta left on a trencher made it clear that all had not yet
supped and that some of the men had probably stayed late in
the village to watch the rioting. But this was the family with
whom the Contessina was perhaps most intimate, so that it
would not displease them to help in her rescue.

'Listen, dear one,' Lucilio said to Clara in a low voice, poking
up the fire to dry her clothes after the dew of the meadows, 'I
will call someone and confide you to the care of one of the
women, and then, by hook or by crook, I will get into the castle
and give them news of you and see how they are there inside.'

Clara blushed under the gaze of the young man. It was the
first time she had received, in a room and by the full light of
the fire, their mute language of love. She blushed without
shame, for it did not seem to her that she had violated any of
the Lord's commandments; and she could not see what difference there might be between loving in secret and confessing
that love to one another.

'Lie down and try to rest,' went on Lucilio. 'I will think in
the meantime of how to give news of what has happened to the
Vice-captain of Portogruaro, so that he may hasten to put an
end to the plots of these rogues. . . . They have not come here

for nothing and I think I can see clearly enough what this sudden zeal of theirs against smugglers means. . . . It is a vendetta or a reprisal, perhaps even a quarrel, cooked up to finish this business of the trial . . . but I will put things in their true light and the Vice-captain will be able to see for himself on which side are the true interests of the Signoria. Meanwhile, Clara mine, stay here in peace and sleep well; to-morrow, if they have not come from the castle to take you home, I will come myself; and who knows what might happen during the night if matters are so pressing. . . .'

'But you . . . don't take any risks for God's sake,' murmured the girl.

'You know me,' replied Lucilio. 'I must be active and try to do something or other even if it were a question of strangers. You can judge for yourself how much more it means when it is a question of your family and our beloved old friend!'

'Poor grandmother,' exclaimed Clara, 'Yes, yes, go and comfort her and then return at once to fetch me, since I shall be waiting here with such an anxious heart.'

'You must go and lie down and I will call one of the women,' said Lucilio.

'No, let them sleep, since I cannot,' replied the girl. 'I wonder at myself and am almost ashamed of myself to stay here and not to go with you.'

'Do what?' exclaimed Lucilio. 'No, for Heaven's sake, don't move from here. Also you must shut yourself in well, since they have been so foolish to leave the doors wide open until midnight! Marianna, Marianna!' he began to shout, going to the door to the stairs.

A moment later a voice replied from above and the scraping of a pair of pattens; and in another minute Marianna, barenecked and bare-armed, descended to the kitchen.

'God forgive me!' she exclaimed, drawing her shift together over her breasts, 'I thought it was my husband! . . . Is it you, Signor Doctor? . . . And the Contessina too! . . . The devil! What has happened? How did you get in?'

'By the open door,' replied Lucilio. 'But this is not the time for chatter, Marianna; the Contessina cannot get into the castle because there is rioting all around. . . .'

'How . . . what sort of riot? . . . Are our men there? . . . Wretches! . . . They have not even eaten their supper! . . . Going out to see what was going on and leaving all the doors wide open too. . . .'

'Listen to me, Marianna,' went on Lucilio. 'Your men will come back. They are in no danger.'

'In no danger, indeed! If you only knew mine, how rash and headstrong he is! . . . He is quite capable of trying conclusions with a whole army, that he is. . . .'

'Very well, but you can be quite sure he will not try anything to-night. . . . I am going in search of them and will send them home. . . . But you, see that nothing is lacking for the Contessina.'

'Oh, poor Signora! What a thing to happen to you! . . . Excuse me for coming down like this, but I really thought it was my husband . . . Wretch! Rushing off like that without his supper and leaving the door wide open. . . . I'll make him pay for it! . . . Only command me, Signora . . . I'm sorry that you will find nothing here that you are accustomed to . . .'

'So, I rely on you, Marianna,' said Lucilio again.

'Naturally! There is no need for orders! I am sorry I am not dressed. But you, Signor Doctor, are accustomed to such things and the Contessina is so good! . . .'

Marianna, busying herself with the fire, displayed two very beautiful shoulders, their whiteness set off by the brown of her arms and face. It may be that she was not too unwilling to show them and for that reason made so many excuses.

'Good-bye . . . love me, love me!' whispered Lucilio in Clara's ear; then, intercepting a glance from her, full of love and hope, he made his way out of the door into the mist that shrouded the countryside. Clara could do no less than follow him to the threshold, and when he was lost to sight, turned back to sit in the kitchen, but not too close to the fire for the heat was great and would have scorched her clothes. Indeed, her head, her pulses burned like embers and her lips and throat

201

were parched as in a fever. Marianna wanted her at all costs to eat a mouthful, but she would not and contented herself with a glass of water. Then she stretched her arm along the back of a chair and rested her head on it as if preparing for sleep. Marianna tried to persuade her to lie down in her own bed, where she had put a newly washed sheet, but seeing that she was wasting her words, the handsome peasant was silent and, having bolted the door, sat down on a stool.

'I wish you would go and lie down,' said Clara, since, however many thoughts and fears she had for herself, she could never have been guilty of forgetfulness for another.

'No, Signora. I must be here ready to open to our men,' replied Marianna, 'otherwise instead of giving a good scolding, it might be that I should get one.'

Clara again rested her forehead on her arm and remained, as they say, dreaming with open eyes, while Marianna, after having nodded for some time, leant over the table and soon began to breathe with the quiet and regular breathing of a robust country girl who sleeps soundly.

Meanwhile, as Signor Lucilio with every precaution against being seen was approaching the moat at the back of the castle, I, sent out as a scout, was proceeding with equal care, intending to wander in such a way as to arrive at the village from quite another direction and thus remove any possible suspicion of the truth. After I had walked about a musket-shot towards the meadow, I seemed to see in the darkness a man's form advancing among the leaves of the vines with the greatest circumspection. I squatted down behind the wheat and watched, protected from the most curious eye by my smallness and the wheat which was all round me with its heavy ears already blond and pendulent. I looked between the stems and the ears and in a clearing flooded by the moonlight, who was it I seemed to see? . . . Signor Lucilio! . . . I had another look to make sure and then decided to make myself known. I rose and advanced towards him carefully, keeping behind the wheat and ready to drop back like a hare into its forme should need arise. Nothing in the world, in my view, could have been more fortunate than this meeting. Signor Lucilio was the confidant of the old Countess and of Clara; he had shown himself well enough disposed towards me on the occasion of my escapade in the marshes; no one could help me in my search better than he could. And as he had the reputation of being a man of sense, I drew the best possible auguries from this meeting. When I was about ten paces from him, 'Signor Lucilio, Signor Lucilio!' I whispered in a quiet and subdued voice that nevertheless strove to make itself heard.

He stood still and listened.

'I am Carlino of Fratta! I am Carlino of the spit!' I went on in the same tone.

He took out of his pocket an object that I later knew was his pistol and came forward looking straight at me. Since I was still in the shadow of the wheat, it seemed he had some trouble in recognizing me.

'Yes, yes, devil take it! It is really me!' I said with some impatience.

'Hush! Silence!' he murmured with a mere thread of voice. 'There is a guard near here and I don't want him to overhear us.'

He meant the guard who had remained alone after his companion had left to act as guide to Lucilio and the Contessina. But solitude is sometimes a bad counsellor and the guard, after a valorous watch of more than half an hour, had finally been vanquished by sleep. Lucilio and I were able to talk in complete security, sure that no one would disturb us.

'Come close and tell me how you got out of the castle and what the news is inside there,' he whispered.

'The news is that they have the fear of the devil for holy oil,' I replied, 'that they have thrown down all the bridges for fear of being killed by the buli of Venchieredo, that the Signora Clara is lost and that since the Ave Maria they have already said two Rosaries. But now they have sent me out to have a look round and try to get news of the Contessina and then to return and report to them.'

'And what were you thinking of doing, little one?'

o                                   203

'*Capperi!* What was I thinking of doing? . . . of going to the inn, pretending to have lost my way, as happened that other time, do you remember? That time of the fever; then listening to what the posse were saying and asking for news of the Contessina from some peasant, and then going back faithfully the way I came out, crossing the moat on a table.'

'You really are a little devil, you know. I never thought it of you. However, you can thank your good fortune that has spared you a good deal of trouble. I have been at the inn, I have taken the Contessina Clara safely to the mill and if you will show me the way to get into the castle, we can give them all the answers together.'

'If I show you the way? All I need to do is to whistle and Marchetto will push the table across. Afterwards leave it to me. You will see how I cross without getting wet and you have only to watch me and do as I do and stay well in the centre of the table.'

'Let's go then.'

Lucilio took me by the hand and keeping close behind some thick hedges, through which it would have been impossible to see us even by daylight, I led him in a flash to the moat. There I whistled as had been arranged and Marchetto ran out quickly and pushed the table across to me.

'So soon?' he said from the other side of the moat, since for the moment surprise made him forget all precautions.

'Quiet!' I replied, showing Lucilio how to make himself comfortable on the table.

'Who is it?' asked the Serjeant, still more surprised since he could now distinguish two figures instead of one in the darkness.

'Friends. Be quiet!' replied Lucilio and then he too, as if brought up to the trade, gave a push that brought us touching the other bank gently.

'It is I!' he said, jumping to the ground. 'And I bring good news of the Contessina Clara.'

'May Heaven be praised!' exclaimed Marchetto, helping me to get the table out of the water.

204

When we entered the kitchen they had only just finished re-peating the Rosary. The fire had gone out, in any case they were in such a state that nobody could have looked after it. Nobody even thought of supper and only Monsignor Orlando every now and then threw an uneasy glance at the cook. Martino, too, had become taciturn and was busy grating his cheese; all the others had faces worthy of a funeral. The ap-pearance of Lucilio was like a ray of sunshine in a storm. An 'Oh!' of wonder, of anxiety and of pleasure echoed round the room and everyone stared at him without asking a single ques-tion, as if uncertain whether he were a man or a ghost. It was therefore up to him to open his mouth first, and the words of Moses when he descended from the Mount were not listened to with greater attention than his. Even Martino stopped his grating, but not being able to hear anything of the talk around him, ended by taking hold of me and making me tell him by signs a part of the story.

'First of all, I have good news of the Contessina Clara,' Lucilio said. 'She had gone out into the fields towards Fossalta to meet the Signora Contessa as usual and was prevented from coming back by the bravos who are on guard every-where. I myself had the honour of taking her to safety in the mill.'

The bravos surrounding the castle on every side rather spoilt the good impression made by the news of Clara. All smiled with their lips at this dove of good tidings, but their eyes were more dismayed than ever, and did not smile at all.

'But we are really besieged then, as if they were Turks!' ex-claimed the Countess, wringing her hands in despair.

'We can console ourselves that the siege is not really so rigorous, since I have been able to get in here,' suggested Lucilio. 'Though it is true that the merit is all Carlino's and if I had not met him I would have had some difficulty in finding my way so quickly and in getting Marchetto to push the table across to me.'

The eyes of the company all turned on me then with a certain respect. At last they understood that I was good for

205

something more than turning the roast, and I enjoyed this little triumph in a dignified manner.

'Were you at the inn, too?' asked the bailiff.

'Signor Lucilio will tell you everything,' I replied modestly. 'He knows more about it than I do, he has had some encounters with these gentry, I believe.'

'And what do they say? Are they thinking of leaving?' the Count asked anxiously.

'They are thinking of staying!' replied Lucilio. 'For the moment at least there is no hope that they will clear out and we must apply to the Vice-captain of Portogruaro to make them put their tails between their legs.'

Monsignor Orlando darted another and more expressive glance towards the cook; the Canon of Sant'Andrea settled his collar with a slight yawn; in both these reverend gentlemen the needs of the body began to cry out more strongly than the afflictions of the spirit. If this were a sign of courage, they were at this time the most valiant hearts in the castle.

'But what do you say? What is your opinion in this crisis?' asked the Count with no less anxiety than before.

'There can be only one opinion,' declared Lucilio. 'Are the walls well manned? Are the doors and windows barred? Are the muskets and the field-pieces at the loop-holes? Are there sufficient men in the castle to look to the defences for a night?'

'To you, to you, Captain!' screamed the Countess, envenomed by the highly unreliable appearance of the Slav. 'Answer the Signor Lucilio! Have you ordered things in such a way that we may consider ourselves safe?'

'That is to say . . .' stuttered the Captain. 'I have only four men including Marchetto and Germano; but the muskets and field-pieces are in order; and I have also distributed the powder . . . for lack of bullets I have used my hunting shot. . . .'

'Excellent! Do you think these rogues are sparrows?' shouted the Count. 'We should do well defending ourselves with bird-shot!'

'For five or six hours even bird-shot will be good enough,' answered Lucilio. 'And if you Signori will be able to hold these assassins at bay until daylight, I believe that the militia of the Vice-captain will then be in time to intervene.'

'Till daylight! How can we defend ourselves until daylight if these desperados take it into their heads to make an assault?' howled the Count, tearing pieces out of his wig. 'If we kill one the blood will go to the heads of the others and we shall all be fried before the Vice-captain has even thought of putting on his boots!'

'I don't see things in quite so dark a way,' replied Lucilio. 'Once one of them has got his deserts, believe me, the others will come to their senses. It is never a bad thing to show one's teeth; and since Captain Sandracca does not seem in his usual spirits, I will take over the defence myself, and I declare and guarantee that I alone will be enough to defend the castle and to put to rout all those braggarts outside.'

'Bravo, Signor Lucilio! You will save us! We are in your hands!' exclaimed the Countess.

Indeed the young man spoke with such assurance that it put a little life back into everyone there; life returned to those faces petrified with fear, and the cook made her way towards the dresser to the great comfort of Monsignor. Lucilio had himself briefly informed of the whole course of the affair; he considered with better judgement that it was some trick of the castellan of Venchieredo to disrupt the investigation by a *coup de main* on the Chancellery, and as the first act of his assumption of authority had all the pertinent papers and documents removed to an inner room of the castle. He then carefully examined the moats, the doors and the windows, and posted Marchetto and Germano at the portcullis; the bailiff he put on guard duty by the stables. Two other Cernide who were the strength of the garrison he placed at the loop-holes that overlooked the bridge, apportioned their duties and gave orders that the first person daring to try and cross the moat should be killed without mercy. Captain Sandracca kept close to the young man's heels while he attended to these provisions, but he had not the heart to put on his usual ugly appearance and it was only due to the signs, grunts and encouragements of his wife that he did not invent a stomach-ache and retire into one of the barns.

'How does that seem to you, Captain?' Lucilio said to him with a rather mocking smile. 'Would you have acted in the same way?'

'Yes, Signor . . . I would have already done all this . . .' stammered the Captain, 'but my stomach . . .'

'Poor thing!' interrupted Signora Veronica, 'he has been working right up till now and it is due to him that these rogues have not already found their way into the castle. But he is no longer as young as he used to be. Work is work, and his strength is no longer equal to his good will.'

'I need rest . . .' murmured the Captain.

'Yes, yes, let him rest as much as he likes,' put in Lucilio. 'He has already shown his zeal nobly and now he can retire under the bedclothes with a clear conscience.'

The veteran of Candia did not need to be told twice; he flew up the stairs like a homing angel and despite the shouts of his wife, who was at his heels, to take care not to fall, in four paces he was in his room, well locked and barred. Having to pass close by the loop-holes gave him a fit of giddiness and he felt much better off between the coverlet and the mattress. For future perils God would provide; those he feared above all were the present ones. Signora Veronica gave full vent to her anger, reproving him for his helplessness, but he replied that it was not his task to deal with thieves and had it been a question of real fighting he would have been at his post.

'These young men, these young men!' exclaimed the valiant fellow, stretching his legs. 'They think they are cut out to be heroes because they have not the prudence to look out for bullets when they show their heads at the battlements. Oh my God! It needs more than that. . . . Veronica, don't leave me, don't go away. . . . I want to defend you as my greatest treasure!'

'Thanks,' replied the woman, 'but why don't you get undressed?'

'Undress! Do you want me to undress while we have this

tempest at our backs? . . . Veronica, keep close to me . . . whoever wants to harm you must first pass over my dead body!'

She too, still dressed, threw herself on the bed and being a brave woman would have gone to sleep had not her husband jumped up at every fly that buzzed, asking her if she heard anything and exhorting her to rely on him and not to go far from her legitimate defender.

Meanwhile, downstairs, a modest repast of eggs and cutlets had calmed the convulsions of the two Monsignors and with their minds once more preoccupied with their former fears they began to ask one another about the number and quality of the assailants, if they were a hundred, three hundred, a thousand, all gallows birds, the best of whom had escaped the noose by the indulgence of the hangman. If they talked about contraband, it was only as a pretext for plunder; to hear them shouting and singing on the piazza, they must all be fighting drunk and therefore reason and mercy were not to be expected from them. The rest of the company exchanged terror-stricken glances at these discussions, and it was worse still when one of the picked men came to report on some sound or movement in the vicinity of the castle.

Lucilio, after having paid a visit to the old Countess and calmed her with some tale about Clara's absence, had returned to comfort these poor devils. He then wrote, and got the Count to sign, a long and very urgent letter to the Vice-captain at Portogruaro and asked permission of the company to go himself and deliver it. Mercy! How could he even suggest it! The Countess almost went on her knees to him, the Count gripped him so violently that he almost tore the seams of his coat, the Canons, the cook, the scullions and the servants surrounded him on every side as if to prevent his leaving. And all with looks, with gestures, with ejaculations and with words besought him to understand that to let him leave would be to deprive them of their last ray of hope. Lucilio thought of Clara, but none the less decided to remain.

But someone was needed to deliver the letter and once again all eyes were turned on me. Taking advantage of the general

209

confusion, I had been all the time in the Pisana's room, enduring her reproofs for the expedition *extra muros* of which I had defrauded her. But as soon as they began calling me, I had the cunning and good fortune to be found on the staircase. They filled my head with instructions and advice, they sewed the letter into my jacket, they embarked me on the same table and there was I, employed for the second time on a diplomatic mission.

It was then exactly ten o'clock at night and the moon shone in my eyes with little modesty, two things that caused me some uneasiness, the first because of the witches of whom I had heard Marchetto talk and the second because of the ease with which I could be observed. But for all that I had the good luck to arrive safe and sound at the meadow.

I trembled a little at first, but reassured myself as I went on, and on entering the mill, as I had been instructed, I assumed a certain air of importance which did me credit. I reassured the Contessina Clara and replied politely to all her questions; then, having told Marianna to wake her eldest son, I took advantage of her absence to remove the envelope from my jacket, and having taken out the letter placed it as if it were of no importance in a satchel. Sandro was a youth some two years older than I, who had displayed a spirit and courage out of the common, for the bailiff had advised me to try and get him to take the letter to Portogruaro.

He accepted the commission without a murmur, threw his jacket over his shoulders, put the letter in his breast and went out whistling as if he were going to water his oxen. The road he had to take towards Portogruaro took him ever further away from Fratta and there was little danger that he would be surprised and intercepted. I had therefore no misgivings and was more than satisfied at seeing all the commissions entrusted to me thus carried out without a hitch; moreover, my ears were still ringing with the praises that they had heard in the kitchen of the castle. Though I had been recommended by Signor Lucilio to keep the Signorina Clara company until the return of the messenger, the ground was burning underneath my feet, all

210

the coming and going, the mystery, the perils had given scope to my childish imagination and I could not stay inactive. I was bent on re-entering the castle, reporting on that part of my task I had already accomplished, coming out once more and finding out what the Vice-captain of Justice had replied.

Clara, when she heard of my intention, asked if I had enough courage to help her too to cross the moat. My little heart beat even more quickly with pride than with uncertainty and I replied with flaming face and tense muscles that I would sooner drown myself than allow even a fold of her dress to get wet. Marianna tried to dissuade her young mistress from this idea with many prudent warnings, but the nail was now well in and I had but to drive it home. I could hardly wait until I should find myself once again in the open.

It was all arranged in a moment; leaving the miller's wife with her prudence, we went out into the fields and thence in a short time reached the moat without mishap. The accustomed whistle, the despatch of the table and the crossing succeeded as perfectly as the others had done. The Contessina was so over-joyed at this surprise that she seemed almost to enjoy crossing the water and she laughed like a child as she knelt down on our contraption. The joy, the wonder, the relief of the family would take too long to tell; but Clara's first thought was to ask about her grandmother; or if not her first thought, it was at least her first word. Lucilio told her that the good old woman, having accepted the story they had told about her, had gone quietly to sleep and it would be better not to wake her again. Then the girl sat down with the rest in the dining-hall; but while the others were listening at the cracks in the shutters at the noises coming from the village, she was speaking to Lucilio with her eyes, thanking him mutely for all that he had done for them. Indeed, all with one voice ascribed to Signor Lucilio the little hope and security that had relieved their spirits after their first dejection. It was he who was ready to reassure them with some good argument, it was he who must provide the castle against a sudden assault, it was he who had conceived that sublime idea of having recourse to the Vice-captain.

211

Then it was my turn to take the limelight. They asked me about the letter and who had been entrusted with it, and all rejoiced to know that within a couple of hours I would return to the mill to hear the reply from Portogruaro. I received a thousand caresses, I was the hero of the hour. Monsignor pardoned me my ignorance of the Confiteor and the bailiff repented having made a roasting-jack of me. The Count turned honeyed glances on me and the Countess never seemed to tire of caressing my neck. Tardy, but merited, justice!

While the whole company was doing all it could to make much of me, the noise outside suddenly increased and Marchetto, the serjeant, with gun in hand and staring eyes, rushed into the dining-hall. What is it? What is the matter? There was a general flurry, an outcry, an asking of questions, an overturning of chairs and candlesticks. The news was that four men had found their way in behind the tower by a disused water-channel; that they had leapt upon him and Germano and that the latter, with two knife wounds in his side, must be in a bad way. Marchetto himself had only just had time to escape, locking the doors behind him. At this news, the screaming and commotion increased threefold; no one knew what to do; they were like quails confined in a dark basket, darting their heads hither and thither without knowledge and without aim. Lucilio exhausted himself in advising calm and courage, but it was like talking to the deaf. Clara alone listened to him and tried to help by persuading the Countess to take heart and trust in God.

'God! God! It is indeed time to rely on God!' exclaimed the Signora. 'Call my confessor! Monsignor, do you think we should commend our souls?'

The Canon of Sant'Andrea, to whom these words were addressed, had no longer soul enough for himself; you can imagine whether he had any intention or possibility of commending those of others!

At that moment the sound of several gunshots was heard and with them cries, noises and threats of men who seemed to be coming to blows in the tower. The confusion knew no limit.

212

The women in the kitchen came in from one direction, the maids, the Pisana and the servants from another; the Captain, more dead than alive, came in supported by his wife and crying that all was lost. The shrieks and prayers of Fulgenzio's family could be heard from without and also those of the bailiff, all asking for refuge in the master's house as the safest place. In the dining-hall the confusion reached its climax: dismayed and frightened voices, prayers, exclamations, weeping women, blaspheming men and exorcizing Monsignors. The Count had lost his shadow, who had deemed the moment opportune to retire even further into obscurity under the table-cloth. The Countess, almost fainting, wriggled like an eel. Clara set herself to comfort her as best she could. I for my part had taken the Pisana in my arms, well content to let myself be cut to pieces before I would relinquish her to anyone.

Lucilio alone kept a cool head in all this turmoil. He asked Marchetto and the servants if all the doors were bolted, and then asked the Serjeant if he had seen the two Cernide before escaping from the tower. The Serjeant had not seen them, but in any case, two men alone were not enough to create the uproar that could be heard outside and Lucilio judged quickly that some fresh incident had occurred. Had his appeal to the Vice-captain already had effect? It seemed too soon, the more so since excess of zeal was not the defect of the militia of that time.

It was, however, clear that some sort of aid had arrived, unless indeed the assailants were so drunk as to discharge their arquebuses at each other. To the complaints of Fulgenzio's family and the bailiff, there was now added the noise of men rapping at the windows and demands that they should open without fear because everything was over. The Count and the Countess were in no way reassured, believing this to be a ruse planned to enter the house by treachery. Everyone crowded anxiously round Lucilio, awaiting counsel and salvation from him alone; the Contessina Clara had taken up a position at the foot of the stairs, intending to run to her grandmother as soon as the danger was imminent. Her eyes replied valorously to

213

the glances of the young man, saying that he should pay attention to the others, since for her part she felt strong and stead-
fast against whatever might happen. I held the Pisana tighter
than ever in my arms, but the little girl, moved to emulation
by my courage, shouted to me to let her go and she would defend herself. Pride so acted on her imagination that she believed she alone was enough against an army. Meanwhile
Lucilio, leaning against the window shutters, asked who was
knocking.

'Friends, friends! From San Mauro and Lugugnana!' replied
many voices.

'Open! I am the Partistagno! The rascals have been driven
off!' broke in another well-known voice, which loosed, if I may
so put it, the breath of all those persons wavering between hope
and fear.

A cry of relief made the walls and windows of the dining-
hall shake and if the whole company had gone mad at the same
time they could not have given way to stranger or more grotesque manifestations of joy. I remember, and I shall always
remember, the Signor Count who, at the welcome sound of that
voice, put his hands to his temples, lifted his wig, and stood
with it thus raised to the skies, as if offering it *ex voto* for the
grace received. I laughed at this, laughed so much, that it was
well for me that the greatness of the relief turned the general
attention away from my person! . . . Finally the doors were
opened, the windows unbarred; lanterns were lit and lamps and
candles, and to the festive splendour of a full illumination, and
amid the sound of triumphal songs, of Te Deums and the most
pious ejaculations, the Partistagno, with his liberating army,
invaded all the ground floor of the castle. The embraces, the
tears, the thanks, the astonishment, were unending; the Countess, forgetting all decorum, had fallen on the neck of the young
victor; the Count, Monsignor Orlando and the Canon of Sant'
Andrea would have liked to imitate her; Clara thanked him
with real emotion for having spared her family who knows how
many hours of dread and uncertainty and perhaps also some
less imaginary evils.

214

Only Lucilio did not join in the jubilation and chorus of praise. Perhaps this liberation did not altogether please him and he would have wished it to come from anywhere save from the quarter whence it had come. However, he was too just and prudent not to mask this untimely feeling of envy and he was the first to ask the Partistagno of the manner and fortune that had led him to this good work. The Partistagno told him how he had come that evening for his usual visit to the castle, though a little later than usual because of the repairing of some of the dykes which had delayed him at San Mauro. The men of Venchieredo had forbidden him to enter and though he had protested loudly against this high-handedness, it had availed nothing; finally seeing that his words did not count a fig and realizing that all this shouting about contraband was only a cover for God knew what schemes, he had decided to turn back and return again armed with quite other arguments than words.

'Though I am not a tyrant by profession,' added the Partistagno, 'even I can, when needs must, do something to make myself felt.'

So saying, he stretched his muscles and displayed some sharp teeth that would not have disgraced a lion.

In fact, he had returned at a gallop to San Mauro and there, having collected a few of his retainers as well as some Cernide of Lugugnana, who were still there working on the dyke, had returned towards Fratta. They had arrived just at the moment when the tower had been taken by the four bravos. Having first easily routed the drunkards who were rioting on the piazza and at the inn, he had set himself to ford the moat with some of his men. After some difficulty they had reached the further side, without those who had occupied the tower troubling themselves to drive them back, since they had been too busy smashing hinges and locks in order to get into the archives. Then, after a few shots exchanged in the darkness, more for show than for need, the four rascals had fallen into their hands and he now held them under guard in the same tower into which they had crept with such barefaced villainy. Among

215

them was the leader of the band, Gaetano. As for the gate-keeper of the castle, he was already dead when the Lugugnana Cernide had found him.

'Poor Germano!' exclaimed the Serjeant.

'Is there really no more danger? Have they all gone? Won't they be back again for their revenge?' asked the Signor Count, who could not realize that such a storm could have dissolved into thin air without some great crashing of thunderbolts.

'The leaders are well handcuffed and will be as quiet as babes till the time comes for the hangman to look after them better,' replied the Partistagno. 'As for the others I bet they will not try to remember the biting smell of the air of Fratta and it will take a lot to get them to smell it again.'

'God be praised!' exclaimed the Countess. 'Signor Baron Partistagno, we will do all in our power to recompense you for the immense service you have rendered us.'

'You are the greatest warrior of modern times!' shouted the Captain, wiping from his forehead the sweat of fear.

'It seems that you thought out a good defence,' replied the Partistagno, 'the windows and doors were so barricaded that not even an ant could have found its way in.'

The Captain was silent and leant against the table to hide the fact that he was without his sword. He made a sign towards Lucilio as if to refer the merit of all the precautions to him.

'Ah, so it was the Signor Lucilio?' exclaimed the Partistagno with a tinge of irony. 'It must be admitted that greater prudence could not have been used.'

This panegyric of prudence in the mouth of one who had conquered by audacity seemed rather too much like raillery for Lucilio not to notice it. His spirit must have risen to great heights to enable him to reply with a modest bow to these ambiguous words. The Partistagno, believing that he had pretty well destroyed him thereby, turned to seek on Clara's face the effect of this fresh triumph over his small, unhappy rival. To his surprise he could not see her, for the girl had already run upstairs to listen at her grandmother's door. But the old

216

woman slept soundly, protected by deafness against the sound of the arquebus shots, and Clara returned to the dining-hall very satisfied with her expedition. The Partistagno looked at her with relish and had in return a glance of real good will that confirmed him still more in his pity for the poor doctor of Fratta.

In the meantime questions about this and that were showered upon him; on the number of the rascals, on the method used by him to cross the moat and, as always happens after a danger is over, everyone enjoyed magnifying it and remembering their emotions at the time. The state of mind of one who has, or thinks he has, escaped a mortal danger resembles that of one who has received a favourable reply to a declaration of love. The same joy, the same loquacity, the same prodigality of everything that is asked, the same lightness of body and of mind; to put it better, all great joys are similar in their effect, in contrast to great sorrows which have a far more varied scale of manifestations. Souls have a thousand senses to feel evil and only one for good and Nature has something of the temperament of Guerazzi that has greater imagination for the miseries than for the rewards of life.

The first to consider that the new arrivals might need some refreshment was Monsignor Orlando; I always think that his stomach rather than his gratitude made him aware of such a need. They say that joy is the most potent of the gastric juices, but Monsignor had digested his supper during his fear and his joy had done no more than stimulate his appetite even more. Two eggs and a small cutlet! More than that was needed to stay the appetite of a Monsignor! . . .

So they set to immediately and made short work of Fulgenzio's piglets. The fear of a long siege had vanished, the cook worked for three, the scullions and the servants had four arms each, the fire seemed disposed to cook everything in a minute. Martino, weeping for the death of Germano, of which he had only just been told by the Serjeant, grated half a pound of cheese in three strokes. The Pisana and I made carnival, happy and content to find ourselves forgotten in the universal rejoicing; as far as we were concerned we would have liked an assault on the castle every month if only to enjoy such excitement. But the memory of poor Germano often intervened to cloud my satisfaction. It was the first time that death had passed close by me since I had reached the age of reason. The Pisana diverted me with her chatter and rebuked me for my uncertain humour.

I replied: 'And Germano?' The little girl sulked, but soon began to chatter again, to ask me for details of my nocturnal expeditions, to try and persuade me that she would have done even better and to join in congratulating me that the cook had deigned to put the roasting-jack into service without fastening upon me to do my usual duties. I forgot my sorrows in this chatter and the petty pride at being regarded as of some importance kept me too occupied with myself and my own prowess to think too much of the dead man.

Midnight had already passed by a good half-hour before supper was ready. No distinctions were made of place or of person. In the kitchen, in the dining-hall, in the pantry, everyone ate and drank as he chose. The families of the bailiff and Fulgenzio were invited to the triumphal banquet and between a mouthful and a toast the death of Germano and the disappearance of the sacristan and the Chaplain required only an occasional sigh. But the dead do not move and the living can be found. Indeed, the little priest and Fulgenzio appeared not long after, so pale and miserable that they looked as if they had been shut up in a flour bin. A great burst of applause greeted their entry and they were invited to tell their stories.

These were in fact very simple. . . . Both of them, so they said, without knowing of the other's intentions, had run at the first arrival of the enemy to Portogruaro to ask for aid and they had in fact only just arrived from there with the aid of Pisa.

'What! Are the noble soldiers outside?' exclaimed the Signor Count, who was still not aware that he had lost his wig. 'Tell them to come in! Come along now, let them in!'

The soldiers were six in number, including a corporal, but in appetite they were the equal of a regiment. They arrived at just the right moment to clean from the platters the last remnants of the roast piglets and to revive the gaiety which had already begun to deteriorate into somnolence. But after they had been satisfied and the Canon of Sant'Andrea had recited an Oremus to render thanks to God for the escape from peril, all thoughts turned seriously to bed. Then, higgledy-piggledy, one here and one there, everyone found his niche, the newcomers in the guest rooms, the others, some in the friars' room, some in the coach-house, some in the hayloft. The following day, soldiers, Cernide and constables received at the order of the Signor Count a large gratuity and everyone returned home after having heard three Masses, in none of which was I called upon to recite the Confiteor.

Thus, after the hurricane had passed, we returned to our usual way of life; the Signor Count, however, had recommended that we celebrate our triumph modestly for it in no way suited him to provoke another reprisal.

With such dispositions of soul, it is no wonder that the enquiry instituted into the revelations of Germano did not advance with much celerity; nor did it appear that there was any real desire to punish the four rascals who were held as the Partistagno's prisoners of war. The castellan of Venchieredo, having been tactfully approached about them, admitted that he had really sent them to track down some smugglers who were said to have taken refuge in the neighbourhood of Fratta, but that his instructions had been exceeded in a manner that was criminally culpable, adding that this did not concern him but the Chancellery of Fratta. The Chancellor for his part did not show any great desire to see the matter through and refrained from forcing the prisoners into dangerous confessions. The example of Germano spoke too clearly and the astute lawyer was a man to take things as they came. He therefore allowed the principal enquiry to slide and in the minor matter concerning the assault on the tower was only too happy to have proved the thorough drunkenness of all the four accused. In this way he hoped to wash his hands of the affair and that

P

the dust of oblivion would providentially accumulate on those ill-omened protocols.

Matters tottered on in this way for about a month, when one evening two Capuchin friars asked hospitality in the Castle of Fratta. Fulgenzio, who was acquainted with all the Capuchin beards of the province, could in no way place these two; but since they declared that they came from Illyria, a circumstance proved by their accents, they were courteously welcomed. Had they come from the moon, nobody would have risked refusing hospitality to two Capuchins on the slender excuse that they did not know them by sight. They excused themselves with pious humility from entering the dining-hall, where that night there was a full assembly, and instead edified the servants with some of their holy hypocrisies and tales of Dalmatia and Turkey, which were the usual stock-in-trade of the friars of those parts.

Then they asked permission to go and lie down, and Martino took them to the room reserved for visiting friars that was separated from my mousehole by the simple board partition and through a crack I watched them enter. A little later the castle was wrapped in the peace of sleep, but I went on watching at the crack because there were certain things about the two Capuchins that piqued my curiosity. As soon as they had entered their room, they shut themselves in with two good turns of the padlock; I then saw them take from under their tunics some implements that, it seemed to me, were labourers' tools, also two strong chisels, two heavy knives and two good pairs of pistols, such as friars are not in the habit of carrying. I hardly dared to breathe for fright, but my curiosity to know what all this apparatus was meant for made me stay at my peep-hole. Then one of them began to break away the stones of the wall opposite with a chisel. This wall backed on to the tower, and one blow after another, the man had soon made a large hole.

'The wall is thick,' observed the other one quietly.

'Three and a quarter feet,' said the one who was working. 'We shall need two and a half hours before we can get through.'

'And if someone discovers us in the meantime?'

'Eh? . . . Well, so much the worse for him! Six thousand ducats will soon pay for a couple of knife thrusts.'

'What if we cannot get out because the gatekeeper wakes?'

'What else will you think of? . . . He is a boy, the son of Fulgenzio. . . . We can soon scare him and get the keys to go out at our ease, otherwise . . .'

'Poor Noni,' I thought, seeing the menacing gesture with which the cut-throat interrupted his work. That hypocrite of a Noni had never been in my good books, especially because of the malicious espionage he carried on to the detriment of myself and the Pisana; but at that moment I forgot his unpleasant habits, as I would even have forgotten the jealous and hypocritical manners of his brother Manichetto. Pity silenced every other feeling; furthermore, the threat touched me also if they once realized that I was watching them through the crack in the partition, but having acquired the taste for adventurous exploits, I hoped that night also to show myself a person to be reckoned with.

I opened the door of my mousehole very carefully and crept on tiptoe into Martino's room. Not wanting or daring to speak, I opened the shutters to let in a little light, for the night was very clear, and then approached the bed and tried to waken him. He leapt up immediately, shouting to ask who it was and what was the matter, but I put my hand over his mouth and signed to him to keep quiet. Luckily he recognized me at once and then, by signs, I got him to follow me and leading him down to the landing on the stairs I gave him an account of the matter. Poor Martino's eyes were as big as lanterns.

'We must wake Marchetto, the Signor Count and the Chancellor,' he said, filled with dismay.

'No, Marchetto will be enough,' said I, with much good sense, 'the others would only make a fuss!'

So we waked the Serjeant, who agreed with me that things should be done quietly and by as few people as possible. The wall on which the Capuchins were working backed on to the Chancery archives, which were in a large dark room on the

221

third floor of the tower, full of documents, rats and dust. The best thing would be to get two strong and reliable men who would seize the two friars as they passed through the hole, blindfold them and bind them securely. And so it was done.

The two men were Marchetto himself and one of his kinsmen, who worked in the castle as a gardener. They made their way very quietly into the archives, using the Count's keys which were always in the pocket of his breeches, hanging in the antechamber. They stood one on the right and one on the left of the spot where the muffled sound of the blows of the chisels could be heard. After half an hour a ray of light penetrated into the archives and the two watchers braced themselves at their posts. They were well armed with hatchets and pistols, but hoped to be able to do without them as the friars imagined themselves to be quite secure and in no danger of being disturbed.

'I can get my arm through,' murmured one.

'Two more blows and the worst is over,' replied the other.

With a little more work they enlarged the hole sufficiently to allow a man to pass with difficulty. Then one of the two friars, he who seemed to be the leader, stuck first his head through, then one and then the other arm and, scrabbling with his hands on the floor, managed to pull his legs through also. But when he least expected it, he felt a friendly force aiding him in this and at the same time received a heavy blow on the chin, his jaws were forced open and a gag jammed between them that almost prevented him from breathing, let alone shouting. A cord tied tightly round his wrists and a pistol held to his head completed the job, and persuaded him not to try and move from the wall against which he was propped. His companion friar seemed a little uneasy at the silence which followed the passage of his chief; but he reassured himself by thinking that he would not breathe a word for fear of being heard and plucked up courage to put his head also through the hole. The second man was treated with even less ceremony than the first. As soon as he had got his head through, Marchetto seized it and pulled so vigorously that he might have torn it off had not his

222

shoulders dislodged some stones from the wall. Gagged and bound in his turn, he was well searched, together with his companion; their arms were taken from them and they were led to a damp cellar, remote and well sheltered from the outside air, where each of them was put in a little cell, like real friars. There they were left to meditate, while we went to wake the family and tell the great news.

You can imagine what amazement, what palpitations and what relief! It was certain that this was some fresh trick on the part of Venchieredo. It was decided to keep the whole affair as secret as possible until an account of it could be sent to the Vice-captain at Portogruaro. Fulgenzio was entrusted with this mission. It caused so great an impression that the castellan of Venchieredo was still waiting for the return of the friars when a company of Slavs surrounded his castle, arrested the Signor Magistrate, and took him duly bound to Portogruaro. Certainly Fulgenzio must have found very decisive arguments to induce the wary Vice-captain to so violent and immediate a resolve. The prisoner, pale with anger and fear, bit his lip at having fallen into such a trap and thought, with tardy prudence, of the fair fiefs that he possessed beyond the Isonzo. The prisons of Portogruaro were very solid, and the speed of his arrest was too significant for him to be able to delude himself with any hopes of escape.

The inhabitants of Fratta for their part railed against the temerity of this tyrant, and great and small rejoiced at the stroke as if it had been their own. An order arrived a few days later to send the four men accused of breaking in by force of arms, and also the two Capuchins and the documents on the Germano enquiry, to a representative of the Most Serene Council of Ten, which marked the climax of the joy of the Count and the Chancellor of Fratta. They breathed again at having cleansed their hands of this pitch and ordered a 'Te Deum' to be sung 'for motives affecting their souls' when, after two months, it came to their knowledge that the six rascals had been condemned to the galleys and the castellan of Venchieredo to ten years' seclusion in the fortress of Rocca d'Anfo,

223

near Brescia, as a criminal convicted of high treason and of conspiracy with foreign rulers against the Republic.

The letters deposited by Germano were in fact part of a secret correspondence carried on between Venchieredo and some Gorizian nobles, in which there was talk of inducing Maria Theresa to take over the Venetian Friuli and assuring her of the support and co-operation of the local nobles. These letters had remained in Germano's possession owing to the difficulties of transport and delivery, and he had omitted to return them, saying that he had destroyed them for fear of the consequences or for some other vital reason. He had thought thus to provide himself with a good defence against his master in case the latter, as was his custom, should try to get rid of him; but destiny had willed that, in spite of his efforts to defend himself, he had instead managed to offend an even more tyrannical and unjust master.

After the criminal trial of Venchieredo, the civil case came up in the courts. But whether it was the prudent policy of the government not to encroach too sharply on the rights of the Friuli nobles, or the skill of the lawyers, or the good will of the judges, it was decided that the jurisdiction of the Castle of Venchieredo should continue to be exercised in the name of the young son of the condemned man, who was then a student at the college of the Scolopi Fathers in Venice. In a word, the civil sentence pronounced against the father was judged not to have effect to the prejudice of the son. Thus it was that, Gaetano and all other obstacles having been removed, Leopardi Provedoni finally received Doretta in marriage. Signor Antonio had to resign himself to this, as also to seeing the Spaccafumo, despite the bans and sentences against him, take part as a greatly honoured guest in the wedding breakfast. The young couple were regarded as the most beautiful seen in the district for the past fifty years and no one took the trouble to count all the fireworks loosed in their honour. Doretta entered triumphantly into the Provedoni household and the beaux of Cordovado had one beauty the more to ogle during the Sunday Mass. If the Herculean strength and the severity of the husband somewhat restrained their homage, the flirtatiousness of the bride continually encouraged them. And everyone knows that in such matters allurements are more potent than fears.

The Chancellor of Venchieredo, left almost absolute master during the minority of the young Magistrate, reflected part of his glory upon his daughter, and certainly on festival days she preferred the arm of her father to that of her husband, especially when she went to preen herself at the festive gatherings around the spring.

My destiny also in the meantime had greatly changed. I was not yet in a position to take a wife, but I was fully twelve years old, and the discovery of the false Capuchins had greatly advanced me in the general opinion. The Countess no longer provoked me, and sometimes even seemed ready to remember our kinship, though she reacted very quickly from these outbursts of tenderness. However, she did not oppose her husband when he took it into his head to apprentice me to the legal profession and to add me as a scribe to the staff of the Chancellery.

PRINTED IN ENGLAND